THE
IRISH SCHOOL
OF MEDICINE

OUTSTANDING
PRACTITIONERS
OF THE
19th CENTURY

DAVIS COAKLEY

TOWN HOUSE

Published in 1988 by
Town House
41 Marlborough Road
Donnybrook
Dublin 4
Ireland

British Library Cataloguing in Publication Data
Coakley Davis, 1946 –
    The Irish school of medicine.
    Outstanding practitioners of the 19th century.
    1. Ireland. Medicine, history
    I. Title
    610'9415

    ISBN 0-948524-08-1

Managing editor — Treasa Coady
Text editor — Elaine Campion
Designer — Bill Murphy
Cover photograph painted by Amelia Stein
Typeset by Printset & Design Ltd, Dublin
Printed by Criterion Press, Dublin

FOR MARY

Acknowledgements

I wish to thank Professor Eamon Sweeney who first encouraged me to write this book. He has also enriched the work with his drawings. The generous support given by the Organising Committee of the XVII Congress of the International Academy of Pathology and by Glaxo Holdings plc has made the publication possible and has allowed the use of so many photographs, including the colour reproductions. In particular I would like to acknowledge the active support of Dr Christopher Pick and Dr David Pratt.

Acknowledgement is due to the following institutions for permission to use material in their possession: Trinity College Dublin, the Royal College of Physicians of Ireland, the Royal College of Surgeons in Ireland, the National Library of Ireland, the National Gallery of Ireland, the Public Record Office of Northern Ireland, Hamilton, Osborne and King, Birmingham Museums and Art Gallery, Downing Street Studios, Farnham Surrey, the Institute of Medical History in Vienna.

Whilst researching this book I received enthusiastic co-operation from Robert Mills, librarian of the Royal College of Physicians of Ireland, and Mary O'Doherty, librarian in the Royal College of Surgeons in Ireland. I also received courteous attention from Stuart O'Seanoir and Áine Keegan, librarians in the Manuscript Room and the Old Reading Room at Trinity College. I am indebted to many others who assisted me, these include Dr Rory O'Moore, Professor Moira O'Brien, Professor Heinrich Holzner, Professor Alan Browne, Dr Eoin O'Brien, Professor J B Lyons, Dr John Fleetwood, Dr Desmond O'Neill, Dr J Bernard Walsh and Professor T Hennessy. The majority of the photographs in the book were taken by David Smyth and I wish to thank him for his interest and co-operation. I also wish to thank David Davison, Patrick Nolan, Peter Butler, Brendan Dempsey, Mary Coakley and Peter Barrow for photographic assistance. My secretary Mary Clarke spent long hours coping with different drafts of the manuscript and I am very grateful for her patience. I wish to thank Mairead Egan who also provided secretarial assistance. It was a pleasure to work with Treasa Coady and Elaine Campion of Town House during the preparation of the book.

The book would not have been possible without the co-operation I received from my wife, Mary. She read everything I wrote during the several stages of the work and her criticism was always most constructive and valuable.

Contents

Illustrations

Introduction

A short and transitory existence has been allotted to our bodies; individuals die, generations pass away, but the common intellect of mankind fears not the same fate, nor shares the same brief mortality.

Robert Graves

At different times since the Middle Ages a number of European cities achieved reputations for greatness as centres of medical practice and teaching. The fame of such centres attracted students from many countries and they became known as schools of medicine. These schools had a great influence on contemporary medical practice and their success was almost invariably due to the motivation of a small group of dedicated teachers who strove for excellence. The schools held their renown for varying lengths of time before entering a decline, then the focus of European medicine would move to another city or country.

The first outstanding school of medicine in Europe was at Salerno in Southern Italy. This school drew on Greek, Latin and Islamic medical traditions and it produced many famous texts. In 1224 the emperor Frederich II decreed that all medical students should be publicly examined by the professors at Salerno on completion of a certain course of study: logic for three years, medicine and surgery for five years, and a year of training with an experienced physician. The Salerno school stimulated development at the universities of Bologna and Padua in Italy and at Montpellier in France. These universities became influential schools of medicine and they dominated medical progress during the Renaissance. The schools of Italy and France rivalled each other and in France leading schools developed in Paris, Strasburg and Toulouse.

In the seventeenth century Irish students began to travel in significant numbers to these European schools for medical teaching and experience. By the end of the century the schools of Italy had lost their pre-eminence and the Dutch University of Leiden was becoming the leading medical centre in Europe. The rise of Leiden was largely due to the great teacher Hermann Boerhaave, whose most significant contribution to medical education was the emphasis he placed on the importance of bedside teaching as opposed to formal lectures. Gerhard van Swieten, a student of Boerhaave, was invited by the empress Maria Theresa to Vienna where he began to develop medical teaching along the lines of Leiden. The

Allgemeines Krankenhaus was built in Vienna in 1784 and became one of the most famous teaching hospitals in Europe. Alexander Munro, also a student at Leiden, brought the teaching of Boerhaave to Edinburgh where he built up a medical school which would become the principal centre of medical education for the English-speaking world in the eighteenth century. This school had a major influence on the development of medicine in Ireland and North America.

The French revolution of 1789 was a significant factor in the emergence of Paris as the leading school of medicine in Europe by the beginning of the nineteenth century. The old theoretical approaches to medical problems were replaced by a new pragmatism. René Laënnec was the greatest physician of this school and his invention of the stethoscope revolutionised medical practice. Another member of the school, Pierre Louis, used statistics to prove that blood-letting was not helpful in healing and he advocated that all treatments should be subjected to scientific evaluation. There were also significant developments in medical education in Germany at this time, with men like Johann Lukas Schönlèin placing great emphasis on the importance of clinical instruction.

The schools of Paris, Edinburgh and Germany all contributed to inspire a group of Irish doctors in the early nineteenth century to bring medical teaching and practice in Dublin to a level of excellence which made it for a time the leading school of medicine in the English-speaking world. Robert Graves, William Stokes, Dominic Corrigan and John Cheyne were the most dynamic physicians of the school. Abraham Colles, Robert Adams, James Macartney, Arthur Jacob, John Houston, William Wilde, Robert Smith, Edward Bennett, Francis Rynd and Francis Cruise were outstanding surgeons of the period. The names of many of these physicians and surgeons are still associated with clinical conditions which they described, such as Graves' disease of the thyroid, Corrigan's sign in incompetence of the aortic valve, Cheyne-Stokes breathing, Stokes-Adams syndrome, Colles' fracture of the wrist, Smith's fracture of the wrist, Bennett's fracture of the first metacarpal, and Houston's valves of the rectum. William Wilde, father of the great wit and dramatist Oscar Wilde, was a pioneer in ear surgery. Francis Rynd gave the first ever subcutaneous injection and Francis Cruise was a pioneer endoscopist. Arthur Jacob was the first to describe the light-sensitive layer of the retina.

The Irish or Dublin school of medicine, as it was sometimes called, was above all a clinical school, the members placing great emphasis on physical signs and the study of pathology. The concepts which they developed form the basis of modern medical teaching in many countries.

CHAPTER 1

Tending and Teaching: Hospitals and Medical Schools in Eighteenth-Century Dublin

In medieval Ireland there were a number of hospitals attached to monastic settlements where the sick poor could receive charity and treatment. The largest of these was the Augustinian hospital of St John the Baptist which was situated in Thomas Street, Dublin. An Augustinian church now stands on the site. This hospital had a charter similar to the charters of the old London teaching hospitals and it was supported by grants from popes and kings. However, it was suppressed in common with all other monastic institutions by King Henry VIII in 1541 and unlike the London hospitals it was not re-established later. As a consequence, provision for the sick poor was very inadequate in Dublin during the seventeenth century.

In the early eighteenth century the suffering of the sick eventually inspired a number of philanthropic individuals to establish hospitals. These became known as voluntary hospitals as they were built, equipped and maintained by private endowment and public subscription. Apart from the Charitable Infirmary which had a number of Irish Catholics among its founders, the main driving force behind the hospital movement were descendants of English settlers who had come to Ireland during the sixteenth and seventeenth centuries as part of the campaigns of Elizabeth, Cromwell and William of Orange. As a consequence of these campaigns the native Irish and the old Norman families had to a great extent been dispossessed of their property and professional opportunities for Catholics were very limited. On the other hand the new Anglo-Irish aristocracy made major contributions to their adopted land in the areas of health, literature and science.

The Charitable Infirmary, known generally as Jervis Street Hospital, was established in 1718 by six surgeons and was the first voluntary hospital in

Ireland and Great Britain. Dr Steevens' Hospital in Steevens' Lane was opened in 1733 with funds bequeathed by Richard Steevens, regius professor of physic at Trinity College. It is a beautiful two-storey building in the Jacobean style, with a large central quadrangle surrounded by a colonnade on the ground floor. Its structure today is practically the same as when its doors were first opened. In 1734 the generosity of Mary Mercer, daughter of another physician, led to the establishment of Mercer's Hospital on the site of an old leper hospital in St Stephen's Street. Handel, the famous German composer, came to Dublin in 1741 and was a benefactor of both Mercer's Hospital and the Charitable Infirmary. Both hospitals had a share in the proceeds of the first performance of the Messiah which was conducted by Handel at the new Music Hall in Fishamble Street on 13 April 1742. Another group of doctors established the Meath Hospital in 1753 and funds from the estate of Sir Patrick Dun, a leading seventeenth-century physician, were used to establish a teaching hospital known as Sir Patrick Dun's Hospital in 1818. The writer Jonathan Swift endowed St Patrick's Hospital for the treatment of patients with mental illness. This hospital adjoins Dr Steevens' Hospital on Steevens' Lane. Building began on the hospital in 1749 and the front and main entrance of the original structure can still be seen today. The Rotunda Hospital in Parnell Square, which is one of Dublin's most famous hospitals and the first maternity hospital in Ireland and Great Britain, owes its existence to the initiative and absolute dedication of another doctor, Bartholomew Mosse. It was founded in 1745 and had a major impact in reducing maternal mortality as it set a high standard of cleanliness and efficiency for Ireland and for the rest of Europe.

The doctors of the eighteenth century who were responsible for building all these hospitals provided their successors with great opportunities for clinical study. The state also developed some institutions in response to the appalling poverty of the time. The City Workhouse and Foundling Hospital was established in 1704 in St James's Street on the site now occupied by St James's Hospital, one of the main teaching hospitals of Trinity College. This institute became the South Dublin Union in the nineteenth century and together with the House of Industry Hospitals (later known as the Richmond Hospital), established in 1773 on the north side of the city, provided medical and social care for the destitute. Both institutions were vast repositories of human misfortune and, like the great Salpêtrière Hospital in Paris, they provided many opportunities for the study of gross pathology.

Although Trinity College, founded in 1592, conferred degrees in medicine in the seventeenth century, it did not have a medical school on its campus. However, in 1705 the university commenced the building of one of the

The old Music Hall in Fishamble St. Dublin, in which the first performance of the Messiah took place.

F. W. Fairholt delin.

1.1 The Music Hall in Fishamble Street

The Music Hall in Fishamble Street was opened in 1741 and could accommodate 700 people. It was designed by Richard Cassell, whom Bartholomew Mosse had brought to Dublin to build the Rotunda Hospital.

Handel was very pleased with the acoustics of the new hall: 'The musick sounds delightfully in this charming room.'

5

oldest medical schools in the British Isles, the School of Physic. The original building was a small, plain structure of red brick and it stood on the site now occupied by the Berkeley Library in the college grounds. It was formally opened in 1711. The College of Physicians was established in 1654 and it was legally entitled to control all medical practice within a seven mile radius of Dublin. Throughout the eighteenth century the School of Physic of Trinity College and the Irish College of Physicians co-operated in developing medical education. Although the School of Physic had some distinguished teachers it was still unable to rival the famous Continental schools. Irish medical students had begun travelling to these schools in the seventeenth century and the practice continued during the eighteenth century. The international character of medical teaching at the time is exemplified by this movement of students between centres as far apart as Leiden, Paris and Prague, a practice which was facilitated by the use of Latin as the language of communication in the medical schools.

Several Irish students went to Prague between 1720 and 1760 where two Irishmen, Professor Jacobus Smith and Professor Wilhelm MacNeven-O'Kelly, held prominent positions. MacNeven-O'Kelly was director of the medical faculty and Smith was rector of the University of Prague. The medical school of the University of Leiden was particularly popular with Irish students during the early part of the eighteenth century, the time when the great teacher Hermann Boerhaave was attracting students to the Dutch medical school from all over Europe. Later in the century, Edinburgh began to develop as a leading medical school and many Irish students went to study there. The Edinburgh school drew its inspiration from Leiden where all five of its original professors had been students of Boerhaave. Alexander Munro was the first professor of anatomy and the driving force of the school following its foundation in 1726. He was succeeded by his son, of the same name, who described the 'foramen of Munro', a small opening between the fluid-filled cavities or ventricles of the brain.

Unlike the Edinburgh school, the School of Physic in Dublin did not flourish in its early years and by the end of the eighteenth century it had entered a serious decline. The establishment of the Irish College of Surgeons in 1784 with its own medical school brought new life into medical education in Ireland. Initially the professors taught from their own homes but in 1789 they acquired a building adjoining Mercer's Hospital. This college attracted many enthusiastic teachers and it formed a direct challenge to the School of Physic at Trinity College.

The Napoleonic wars created a growing demand for military surgeons and this demand stimulated the growth of the College of Surgeons. It also

By courtesy of Hamilton, Osborne and King

1.2 Dr Steevens' Hospital

Dr Steevens' Hospital and the Royal Hospital Kilmainham were the only two hospitals in eighteenth-century Dublin to adopt the courtyard design, the traditional approach to hospital architecture on the Continent at that time. Dr Steevens' Hospital ceased to function as a general hospital in 1987. It was acquired by the Eastern Health Board for their headquarters.

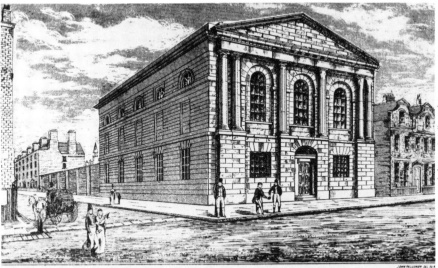

THE ROYAL COLLEGE OF SURGEONS IN 1810.

From Cameron's *History of the Royal College of Surgeons in Ireland* (1886)

1.3 The Royal College of Surgeons in Ireland in 1810

The military campaigns of the period stimulated a great demand for army and naval surgeons. Irish surgeons took advantage of this situation to obtain substantial grants from the treasury so as to build and equip their new college at the corner of York Street and St Stephen's Green.

led to the establishment of several small, private medical schools in the city. These new schools trained surgeons mainly for the British military and naval services. Napoleon could therefore claim some of the credit for the stimulus behind the development of medical teaching in Dublin. Ironically, he was later to benefit himself, as at various times during his captivity he was cared for by five Irish medical officers. One of these, Dr Barry O'Meara, treated him with great sympathy and sensitivity during his imprisonment on the island of St Helena. During their first conversation, just five weeks after the Battle of Waterloo in 1815, Napoleon ascertained that O'Meara had studied in Dublin and London, so he asked him which was the best school of physic. ' "I replied that I thought Dublin the best school of anatomy and London of surgery." "Oh!" said he, smiling, "You say Dublin is the best school of anatomy because you are an Irishman." "I answered that I begged pardon, that I had said so because it was true, as in Dublin the subjects for dissection were to be procured at a fourth of the price paid for them in London, and the professors were equally good." '[1] There is probably some truth in this as 'body snatching' was a thriving business in Dublin at the beginning of the last century; there was actually an export trade to some of the British medical schools, the bodies being shipped in boxes labelled 'pianos' or 'books'.

The small private schools in Dublin were in direct competition with each other and they prospered or failed in accordance with the standard of their teachers. Some schools had special attractions to draw students. John Kirby, a very popular teacher, had a school in Peter Street and he was renowned for the fact that during some of his demonstrations he would shoot at a corpse propped against the wall of the lecture room. The surgeon and his pupils then rushed forward and operated on the body, dressing the wounds just as they would do on a battlefield. Many of the leading surgeons ran small schools in the stables or mews of their own private houses. The main emphasis of most of these schools was on the teaching of anatomy and surgery and the teachers, although good, enjoyed only a local reputation.

As time progressed a number of teachers from the small private schools came together to form larger private schools with higher standards. The Irish College of Surgeons also flourished and a fine new building was erected on St Stephen's Green to accommodate the expanding student population. This new college was opened in 1810.

CHAPTER 2

Macartney and Cheyne: Champions of Anatomy and Pathology

Faced with opposition from all sides, the School of Physic was in great difficulties at the beginning of the nineteenth century. However, it was saved by the appointment of one of the most dynamic professors the school has ever possessed. This was James Macartney, who was appointed professor of anatomy and surgery in 1813. He was filled with a determination to make the School of Physic equal if not superior to the schools of London and Edinburgh. Within three years of his appointment the intake of new students had risen to ninety; his lectures became so popular that he had 'not only to repeat each of his daily lectures twice over, but in each lecture he had to show and describe his specimens twice, as only half of the class could see them at one time'.[1]

Macartney was born in County Armagh in 1770. While still a youth he became involved with the United Irishmen, a republican movement. However, when the movement became a secret society in 1794 Macartney refused to take the required oath. He remained a friend of the revolutionaries Wolfe Tone and John Sheares, but he was unenthusiastic about the proposal for an armed rebellion. He moved to Dublin in 1794 where he became an apprentice to Professor Hartigan, the professor of anatomy in the School of Physic, and he began his studies in anatomy in the College of Surgeons. He moved to London in 1796 where he worked with the famous British surgeon John Abernethy. His talent was recognised and he was appointed to the lectureship in comparative anatomy at St Bartholomew's Hospital in 1800. Four years later Charles Bell, whose name is associated with palsy of the facial nerve and who was then at the height of his fame, invited Macartney to Edinburgh to work with him as a colleague, but Macartney declined the offer. His scientific endeavour was rewarded in 1811 when he was elected a fellow of the Royal Society.

Two years later, when Macartney applied for the chair of anatomy in the School of Physic in Dublin, he submitted references from two leading British medical men, Sir Astley Cooper and Sir Benjamin Brodie, and from the famous scientist Sir Humphrey Davy, the discoverer of nitrous oxide (laughing gas) and the inventor of the miner's lamp. Macartney had attended Davy's lectures during his period of study in London. However, he was not the candidate favoured by the board of Trinity College or the College of Physicians, possibly because of his previous connections with the United Irishmen. Whitley Stokes, an able physician who had also associated with the United Irishmen movement, campaigned for Macartney's appointment. An equally strong campaign was initiated by the opposition and 'active and extraordinary exertions were made to bias the electors in their decision'.[2] Macartney was elected as his credentials could not be ignored, but his relationship with the establishment in Trinity College and the College of Physicians remained very strained throughout most of his career. Soon after his appointment he upset his physician colleagues by suggesting that the final medical examinations should be held in English rather than in Latin and he annoyed them further by performing autopsies on their patients without their permission.

In the summer of 1816 Macartney left Dublin to visit European medical centres. On his way he stopped for a while in London where he met the surgeon Sir Benjamin Brodie and the botanist Robert Brown. Then he travelled on to Paris where he visited the Hotel Dieu and there made the acquaintance of the famous surgeon Guillaume Dupuytren, whom he described as 'an active sensible man who did his work with great regularity'.[3] He also visited Baron Larrey, Napoleon's surgeon, and he was shown an unusual case of a man who had a wound in the chest wall through which the naked heart could be touched. This injury had resulted from a gunshot wound received during the campaign in Belgium. The man was recovering and the wound was gradually closing. Macartney stayed some time in Paris before he proceeded across the north of France to Brussels. It was just three months since the Battle of Waterloo and the hospitals were still full of wounded soldiers. He visited these hospitals regularly and met many doctors from several different countries. He collated the information received from them concerning the requirements for medical graduation in their respective countries and he also visited several Belgian medical schools. All these contacts were to prove very useful to him later when his own students set out for the Continent in search of postgraduate experience. He returned to Dublin with renewed determination to improve

2.1 James Macartney (1770-1843)

Macartney was a great medical pioneer and educational reformer. He was the first systematic lecturer on pathology in Ireland and Britain. According to his biographer, Macalister, others who came after him became famous by practising his methods and 'by adopting his very phrases'.

the facilities for medical education.

Macartney placed great emphasis on the importance of studying pathology. He made a major contribution to the development of the School of Physic and his teaching inspired many of his students to practise the science as well as the art of medicine. At the end of a session in 1822 his pupils invited Macartney to a dinner in a Dublin hotel. In responding to a toast Macartney emphasised that he 'always felt when among students as a fellow student, every day showing him how much is to be learned in the science of medicine'. Dr Arthur Jacob, one of the demonstrators in his department, also spoke:

> Allusion has been made to the rising celebrity of the School of Medicine and Surgery in Dublin, and I shall not hesitate to assert that the cause of that celebrity may be traced to the indefatigable exertions of your guest and preceptor, Dr Macartney. In stating this, far be it from me to undervalue the labours of our other learned Professors, to whom you are all so much indebted; but gentlemen, the character of every school of medicine in Europe has risen and fallen, with that of its anatomical instruction, and if Dublin should become the seat of a great School of Medicine, the foundation of that school must be dated from 1813, when the heads of the University placed the present Professor in the anatomical chair.[4]

2.2 The medical school in Trinity College,
opened in 1825

On 1 November 1825 Macartney delivered his inaugural lecture in the new school; he claimed that members of the board of Trinity College had 'bestowed a more valuable gift upon the community by building this house than if they had founded ten hospitals'. Although this building was largely replaced during a period of further development later in the century, elements of the original structure can still be seen today.

These words were prophetic as Dublin was soon to become one of the leading medical centres of Europe. However, posterity has not been as generous as Jacob, and Macartney has never received the credit due to him.

Macartney's energy and drive led eventually to the building of a new anatomy school in Trinity College in 1823. Even this was not free of controversy as Macartney fought with the architect over the inadequacies of the building; on one occasion, to articulate his displeasure, he broke his umbrella over the architect's head. Eventually in 1825 the building was finished and Macartney gave a special inaugural lecture. He invited members of the board of Trinity College to attend and he reserved some seats in the front of the hall for them. However, the seats remained empty throughout the lecture. According to his biographer, Macalister, the class which assembled during the first session in the new building was the largest that had ever attended the lectures of any medical teacher in Dublin.

In 1813, the year that Macartney took up the chair of anatomy in the School of Physic, John Cheyne commenced his duties as the first professor of medicine in the Royal College of Surgeons. Cheyne was a Scotsman from Leith near Edinburgh. His father and several of his forebears had been doctors. His own career started at the age of thirteen when he began to attend his father's poor patients. He was sent to ensure that they were supplied with medicines, to bleed them, to dress their wounds and to report on their condition. Later he went to Edinburgh where he obtained his medical degree in 1795. Cheyne first came to Ireland as a twenty-one year old army medical officer in a brigade of horse artillery which was sent to help quell the Irish rebellion of 1798. He was present at the battle of Vinegar Hill in County Wexford, one of the most crucial and bloodiest of the uprising, when the Irish army was defeated.

In 1799 he returned to Scotland where he worked as an assistant to his father. He also studied pathology in Edinburgh under Sir Charles Bell who encouraged him and stimulated in him a desire to strive for distinction. Cheyne published three books following nine years' work in Scotland: these were his *Essays on the Diseases of Children* (1801), which was produced in collaboration with Charles Bell, who also illustrated the work; *Essays on Hydrocephalus Acutus* (1808), which contained the first detailed description of the condition, and *The Pathology of the Larynx and Bronchia* (1809).

Cheyne never lost his interest in Ireland and after nine years he decided to revisit Dublin. He found that the Dublin physicians relied chiefly upon symptomatology for their diagnoses and that they paid little attention to pathology. Because of this, much of the purely medical practice was passing into the hands of surgeons. Cheyne concluded that there were opportunities

2.3   John Cheyne (1777-1836)

Cheyne's detailed account of a number of medical conditions gained him a world-wide reputation. Eventually his practice became so large that he could not cope because of poor health, so he left Dublin in 1831 and settled in Sherrington, a small village in Buckinghamshire, England.

2.4   Charles Bell (1774-1842)

Charles Bell, who was trained in anatomy and surgery by his brother John, was a pioneer in the field of neuroanatomy. Both brothers experienced bitter opposition in the University of Edinburgh from a faction led by James Gregory, the professor of medicine. In 1804 Charles left to practise in London but he returned to Edinburgh in 1836 to take the chair of surgery.

15

for a physician in the city so he decided to stay. He was appointed physician to the Meath Hospital in 1811 and two years later he was appointed professor of medicine in the College of Surgeons.

Cheyne's lectures were mainly on military surgery and medicine and they were attended by army and naval surgeons as well as by the regular pupils of the college. In 1812 he published a book entitled *Cases of Apoplexy and Lethargy with Observations of Comatose Diseases*. Today, one of the most widely read books on the same subject is *Diagnosis of Stupor and Coma* by the American neurologists Fred Plum and Jerome Posner. They honour Cheyne by using the title page of his book as a frontispiece for their own work.

In 1815 Cheyne resigned his position in the Meath Hospital and moved to the House of Industry Hospitals (subsequently known as the Richmond Hospital) in Brunswick Street. Here he concentrated on the treatment of fevers and established a clinical school with a museum of pathological specimens. As there was no medical journal in Ireland at the time Cheyne, in collaboration with others, launched the *Dublin Hospital Reports* in 1815. Cheyne's papers on fever, which he published in this journal, set the tone for the subsequent labours of the Irish school of medicine, as models of clinical observation presented with clarity and accuracy. In 1818 Cheyne contributed a paper entitled 'A case of apoplexy in which the fleshy part of the heart was converted into fat'. This contribution contained the first description of the breathing pattern which would later become known as Cheyne-Stokes Respiration:

> The only peculiarity in the last period of his illness, which lasted only eight or nine days, was in the state of the respiration. For several days his breathing was irregular. It would entirely cease for a quarter of a minute, then it would become perceptible, though very low, then by degrees it became heaving and quick, and then it would gradually cease again. This revolution in the state of his breathing occupied about a minute, during which there were about thirty acts of respiration.[5]

After the publication of this paper, Cheyne began to concentrate on developing a lucrative private practice at his home in Ely Place. In all, five volumes of the *Dublin Hospital Reports* were published, and Cheyne was involved in producing four of them. The last issue, which appeared in 1830, was edited by Robert Graves, a very promising young physician who was rapidly becoming the torch bearer of Dublin medicine.

CHAPTER 3

Robert Graves and
the Practice of Humanity

Robert Graves was the son of Richard Graves, a celebrated fellow of Trinity College who filled in turn the chairs of divinity, law and Greek. The Graves family has made significant contributions to Irish and indeed international intellectual life over several generations. Members of the family have been scientists, divines, doctors, writers and poets, including the poet Robert Graves in our own time.

The physician, Robert Graves, was born in Dublin in 1796. He entered Trinity College in 1811 and after a brilliant undergraduate career he graduated in arts in 1815 and medicine in 1818. As a student he came under the influence of James Macartney, the professor of anatomy and surgery, who encouraged him to study pathology. Under Macartney's guidance Graves became proficient in anatomy, which was unusual for someone intending to be a physician. At that time post-mortem examinations were generally performed by a surgeon.

After qualifying, Graves spent three years on the Continent where he survived many adventures. On one occasion he was imprisoned in a jail in Vienna for ten days on suspicion of being a spy. He didn't have his passport with him when he was arrested and because of his flawless German his captors would not believe that he was Irish. In 1819 Graves travelled by coach across the Alps through the Mont Cenis pass into Italy. On the journey he was joined by a rather taciturn traveller whom Graves assumed at first to be a sailor. Every so often his companion took a notebook from his pocket and made quick sketches which Graves discovered, to his surprise, were of the cloud formations which were passing overhead. This intrigued the young doctor as he was also accomplished in sketching and the two men became very friendly. It transpired that Graves' companion was the famous artist William Turner. For several weeks the two men travelled together throughout Italy, stopping to paint at different locations and often returning to the same place for several days. They remained in Florence for some time before journeying south to Rome. On arriving at a new location Turner usually contented himself on the first day with making a careful outline of the scene. Then, while Graves painted diligently, Turner just looked on, apparently doing nothing, until at a particular moment, often after a few days, he would suddenly exclaim, 'There it is!.' He then worked rapidly until he was satisfied that he had recorded the particular effect he wished to fix in his memory.

> When our work was done we compared drawings, the difference was strange; I assure you there was not a single stroke in Turner's drawings that I could see like nature; not a line nor an object, and yet my way was worthless in comparison with his. The whole glory of the scene was there.[1]

The Irish physician was one of the few men in whose company Turner is known to have worked.

Graves decided to visit Sicily and he travelled on a small ship with only one other passenger, a Spaniard. The ship ran into very bad weather and was soon in difficulties. The pumps failed and it began to fill with water. The captain and the crew decided to leave on the only small boat on the ship but there was no room for the two passengers. Graves argued that a small boat had no chance of survival on the raging sea. As the crew would not listen, Graves broke in the side of the boat with an axe saying 'If that be the case let us all be drowned together. It is a pity to part good company'. The captain drew a dagger but he did not advance on the young doctor. Graves was soon giving directions and he replaced the perished valve-leather of the pumps with pieces cut from his own footwear. The pumps began to work again and eventually the storm abated.

Following the peace settlement at the Congress of Vienna in 1815, when Napoleon's victors 'redrew' the map of Europe, literature and science began to develop again and medicine in particular made great progress. Graves became familiar with the teaching and discoveries of the great medical schools. He formed friendships with the leading physiologists and physicians of Europe and he continued to correspond with many of them during his life. He studied under Stromeyer and Blumenbach at Gottingen, Cohleston in Copenhagen, and Hufeland and Behrend in Berlin. He also visited the medical centres of Vienna, Paris, Florence, Venice and Rome. During all these travels he was exposed to the liberal ideas of the period.

3.1 Robert Graves (1796-1853)

Graves, apart from being a remarkable clinical observer and writer, became one of the most dynamic and famous teachers that medicine has known.

Graves was an advocate of civil and religious freedom and possessed great integrity:

> Loving truth for its own sake, he held in unconcealed abhorrence, all attempts
> to sully or distort it; and he never withheld or withdrew his friendship from
> any, even those below him in education and social rank, if he found in them
> the qualities which he loved, and which he never omitted to honour.[2]

While on the Continent Graves spent most of his time studying in Berlin and was deeply impressed by the method of clinical teaching employed there. The training of doctors in clinical methodology left much to be desired when Graves was a student in Dublin. Often information had to be acquired on one's own initiative at the hospital or by standing at the edge of a large group of students, listening to the physician expound in Latin. In the German teaching hospitals, on the other hand, patients were assigned to senior students who examined them very carefully. When the physician made his ward round the student in charge of each patient would read aloud from his notes and the physician would make any corrections necessary. A case conference took place after the round when the therapy proposed by the students would be analysed. The prescriptions were then corrected

3.2 The Meath Hospital

The original Meath Hospital was opened in 1753 in a house on the Coombe. The building, illustrated here, was completed in 1822 on a site off Heytesbury Street which was known as the 'Dean's Vineyard' and which was acquired from the dean and chapter of St Patrick's Cathedral. It was the hospital which Graves and Stokes made famous and it still functions as a hospital today.

From Cameron's History of the Royal College of Surgeons in Ireland (1886)

for any 'inaccuracy or inelegance'.[3] The students were expected to know the cost of the prescribed medication so that they might learn 'to accommodate as far as possible the expense of the remedies to the circumstances of their patients'.[3] When Graves returned to Dublin in 1820, after a few months in Edinburgh, he decided to adopt and develop the German method of bedside teaching in Dublin. He became the pioneer of this bedside approach to medical education in Ireland and Great Britain. His work also had a major influence on medical teaching in America.

Graves was appointed visiting physician to the Meath Hospital in 1821 and from the start he made a strong impression on all who met him. He had a striking appearance, being tall, of dark complexion and with very refined and expressive features. Andrew Young was a student at the Meath Hospital around this time and he remembered his first encounter with Graves:

> As far as I learned from the conversation around me, which was carried out in loud tones and with much hilarity, it appeared that Dr Graves had just returned from the Continent (Germany, I think) and teemed with information, professional and otherwise, the result of his foreign travel. The facility with which he answered the many questions put to him, and the amount of information he conveyed, so clearly and in such charming language, made a very strong impression on my mind as a youngster; and, as I observed him in after life, each succeeding year, increased my admiration of his learning, his assiduity and the depth of his professional information.[4]

Young recorded that it was Graves who first introduced the stethoscope to Ireland. This stethoscope was a piece of timber (probably elm) around thirty to thirty-five centimetres in length and about seven centimetres in diameter, with a hole drilled through it from top to bottom. There was no earpiece and no attempt at ornamentation. Graves frequently referred to it as the 'cylinder' and as Young remembered:

> It was amusing to watch the shakes of the head as this bludgeon passed from hand to hand among the pupils, and to listen to the comments made by them, whilst Dr Graves was holding forth in its praise.[5]

Young also recalled the secret amusement of the students when they watched a senior member of the Meath staff listen to a chest at Graves' invitation. It was obvious to the watching students that the apertures of the ear and the stethoscope were at least an inch apart as he pressed it against his head, yet when he looked up eventually he announced with confidence that 'he heard the sounds as they were described to him quite plainly'.[5]

Graves approached his new post with great energy, often beginning ward rounds at 7.00 am and being led through the hospital on dark winter mornings by students carrying candles. He encouraged all his students to place particular emphasis on the study of pathology. Young recalled carrying out a post-mortem examination on patients who had died the previous night:

> There are few of us who like to be inhaling the emanations from a body recently dead from fever, or other such ailments, on empty stomachs, and often I have been busy for hours, until the afternoon, and alone, when he would return to the dead room, where I had been making careful dissections of the diseased parts. He would scrutinise these carefully, and make his remarks aloud for my instruction, and finally address me to this affect, 'Young, this is the true way to study pathology. Here we see the changes which caused the symptoms we watched at the bedside with so much anxiety and which are still fresh in our memory; and we can mentally follow each in its progress, until death resulted'.[6]

Graves constantly exhorted the students to spend time on the wards gaining practical experience. There could be no substitute for this aspect of training.

> The human mind is so constituted, that in practical knowledge its improvement must be gradual. Some become masters of mathematics, and of other abstract sciences, with such facility, that in one year they outstrip those who have laboured during many. It is so, likewise, in the theoretical parts of medicine but the very notion of practical knowledge implies observation of nature. Nature requires time for her operations; and he who wishes to observe their development will in vain endeavour to substitute genius or industry for time .... Students should aim not at seeing many diseases every day; no, their object should be constantly to study a few cases with diligence and attention; they should anxiously cultivate the habit of making accurate observations.[7]

It was a dangerous time to be either a medical student or a doctor, as many became victims of the epidemic diseases which were rampant at the time. Graves, however, never hesitated to put his own life at risk in the service of his fellow countrypeople. At that time the Irish population was very dependent on the potato as a source of food. This dependence would eventually lead to devastation when the potato crop failed for a number of years in succession between 1846 and 1849. However, there were several smaller famines before that time. One of these occurred in 1822 when the potato crop failed, forcing thousands of rural people to crowd into the cities in search of work. Infectious diseases spread rapidly through the weakened population, particularly in the west of Ireland. Three physicians attached to the fever hospital in Galway died. Graves and a number of other Dublin doctors went to the fever-stricken city and he later described the terrible scenes he witnessed:

> The terror of the infection was so great, that it was not unusual for persons to guard their mouths with handkerchiefs while passing those houses in which a case of fever was known to exist, and it has happened to us more than once to observe the like precaution taken, when they had, what they seemed to consider, the misfortune of meeting any of our medical party in the streets.[8]

His experiences at this time made such a deep impression on Graves that he subsequently took a great interest both in the treatment of fever patients and in the conditions of service of their doctors.

In 1824 Graves joined with some medical and surgical colleagues to found a private medical school in Park Street (now Lincoln Place). It became one of the most successful private schools in Dublin and was for a time a rival to the College of Surgeons. By 1833 it had about 140 students attending its classes.

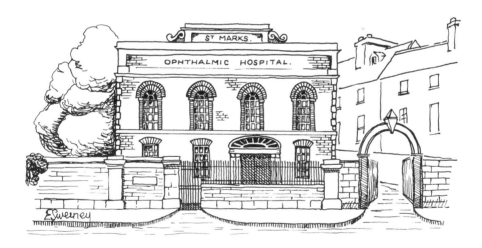

3.3 Park Street School (1824-1849), later St Mark's Ophthalmic Hospital (1850-1904)

The Park Street School was situated at the rear of Trinity College, in close proximity to the School of Physic. Park Street was then a red light district; years later when it was 'purified from its moral filth' the name was changed to Lincoln Place. It closed in 1849 when the principal proprietor, Hugh Carlisle, was appointed professor of anatomy in Belfast.

In 1827 Graves was appointed to the King's professorship of the Institutes of Medicine in the School of Physic. There were three King's professorships (Medicine, Institutes of Medicine and Materia Medica) and they were funded from the Sir Patrick Dun's bequest to the College of Physicians. The School of Physic Act, the last Act passed by the Irish Parliament in College Green in 1800, had united these professorships and the four professorships in the university (Medicine, Anatomy and Chirurgery, Botany and Chemistry) into a 'Complete School of Physic'. The three King's professors lectured at Sir Patrick Dun's Hospital where the College of Physicians was based and the four university professors lectured in the Anatomy House in Trinity College. Graves' professorship covered physiology, pathology and therapeutics. Sir William Wilde was a student of Graves and he recalled that at Graves' lectures in Sir Patrick Dun's Hospital 'the attention that had flagged at an earlier hour of the day was aroused by the absorbing interest of the subject and the energy of the lecturer'.[9]

Erinensis, who wrote sarcastic and satirical sketches on Dublin medicine for the medical journal *The Lancet* and who is thought to have been Dr Peter Hennis Green, described one of Graves' introductory lectures in less flattering terms:

> He passed to the professor's chair with an alacrity of motion and he opened on his audience in a tone of impassioned perusal from a manuscript, which to persons accustomed to less enthusiastic modes of address, and unacquainted with his warm temperament, might be painfully startling. His countenance, naturally expressive of much latent emotion, even in a state of quiescence, when thoroughly excited as it then evidently was, by the working of his feelings, together with the accompaniment of a husky, sepulchral voice, strained to the highest pitch, and let loose on his audience without much regard to modulation, struck us, we confess, with a degree of surprise, a little too electric to be agreeable.[10]

Graves escaped lightly when this is compared to some of the sketches of other leading members of the medical profession at that time. In the same article Green said that Graves was experiencing difficulties in introducing the new clinical teaching methods, and having given Graves some credit for introducing a number of reforms, Green went on to express doubts about the practicality of assigning the care of patients to senior students:

> In Edinburgh, where the closest approximation of this excellent ordinance has been made, the professors confess that any further extension of this mode of tuition is really impracticable among the pupils and patients of Great Britain. The former are necessarily a migrating body in this country, different parts of their education being acquired in different schools, so that

they cannot well comply with any well organised plan of instruction; and the latter are, perhaps, too deeply imbued with that restive selfishness, generated by free political institutions, ever to suffer themselves to become the passive instruments of experiment for the benefit of students. These are obstacles, to the removal of which, even the laudable zeal of Dr Graves could not be supposed competent. He still however persists, with the most praise-worthy perseverance, in the prosecution of his design, and has, we are told relinquished, in a great measure, his private practice, since his election to a professor's chair, that he might have more leisure to follow up his favourite pursuits.[10]

Graves himself admitted that he faced considerable opposition in introducing his reforms. Eleven years after returning to Ireland, he voiced some of his frustrations during a lecture:

Bedside teaching was ridiculed in every possible manner; even now it may be doubted whether its well-wishers are as numerous as might be expected. It is still opposed by several narrow-minded persons, whose opinions have much weight with the pupils.[11]

William Stokes, one of Graves' first pupils, described the unsatisfactory position of the student before Graves' reforms:

He was kept at a distance; no one cared to instruct him, to show him how to teach himself, to make him familiar with bedside teaching and the 'ways of the sick', to exercise his powers of perception, to train his mind to reason rightly on the phenomena of disease — and, lastly, to make him learn the duty as well as the pleasure of original work.[12]

In 1828 Graves spent some months at the Charitè and St Louis Hospitals in Paris and the following year he studied for a period in Hamburg. He was greatly impressed by the democracy of French medicine, which was one of the products of the Revolution. The doctors were not like those in Dublin, provided with two vocabularies — one for the rich and the other for the poor. The Italians, he found, were less circumspect with their language. He was dismayed when he saw a woman with cancer of the uterus break down and weep when she heard a doctor tell his students in detail of her poor prognosis. Graves told his students that 'One of the most important duties of a surgeon or physician is the practice of humanity'.[13] He followed the German and French custom of using the vernacular when the outlook for the patient was good and Latin when the prognosis was bad. Graves kept himself abreast of the developments on the Continent and there can be little doubt that part of the reason for his success as a teacher was his firm belief in the importance of postgraduate education:

> We may hold that there can be nothing more likely to excite the student to love his profession, and to labour for it, than to see his instructor remaining as his fellow student; young in mental energy, and in the desire and acquisition of knowledge; for thus only is it given to us to resist the advance of time.[14]

Many leading Irish doctors, including Graves himself, were now publishing an increasing amount of original work. In a lecture to his students in 1834 Graves drew the attention of his audience to this significant change:

> It is not unusual to find the publications of France, Germany, Italy and England simultaneously announcing the same discovery, and each zealously claiming for their respective countrymen an honour which belongs equally to all. I am sorry to say that, with some splendid exceptions, this interesting and innocent controversy has been carried on by other countries while Ireland has put in no claim for a share of the literary honours awarded to efforts of industry or genius. But, Gentlemen, I hope that this state of inaction, this state of mental torpor, has ceased and that the time has passed away when we could not point out among our brethren any who had advanced the boundaries of the medical sciences, and thus promoted the interests of humanity.[15]

Within a year of this lecture, Graves' most famous paper was published in the *London Medical and Surgical Journal*. The paper bore the title 'Newly observed affection of the thyroid gland in females'. This was the classic description of exophthalmic goitre (Graves' Disease):

> I have lately seen three cases of violent and long continued palpitations in females, in each of which the same peculiarity presented itself, viz; enlargement of the thyroid gland .... A lady, aged twenty, became affected with some symptoms which were supposed to be hysterical. This occurred more than two years ago; her health previously had been good. After she had been in this nervous state about three months, it was observed that her pulse had become singularly rapid. This rapidity existed without any apparent cause, and was constant, the pulse being never under 120, and often much higher. She next complained of weakness on exertion, and began to look pale and thin. Thus she continued for a year, but during this time she manifestly lost ground on the whole, the rapidity of the heart's action having never ceased. It was now observed that the eyes assumed a singular appearance, for the eyeballs were apparently enlarged, so that when she slept, or tried to shut her eyes, the lids were incapable of closing. When the eyes were open, the white sclerotic could be seen to a breadth of several lines, all around the cornea. In a few months the action of the heart,

continuing with increasing violence, a tumour, of a horse-shoe shape, appeared on the front of the throat and exactly in the situation of the thyroid gland.[16]

On the Continent this condition is known as Von Basedow's disease, named after Carl von Basedow who described a case in 1840, five years after Graves' description.

Graves was the first to describe the condition known as angioneurotic oedema, doing so in 1843 in the first edition of his *Clinical Lectures*, nearly forty years before Heinrich Quincke, professor of medicine at Kiel, published his description. He was also the first to describe peripheral neuritis which he saw in epidemic form in Paris in 1828. It was Graves who established the science of pulse-taking, as the distinguished American physician Weir Mitchell wrote 'the familiar figure of the doctor, watch in hand, came to be commonplace'. He kept regular records of the pulse and related the findings to his clinical observations. In 1830 he published a paper entitled 'On the effects produced by posture on the frequency and character of the pulse in health and disease' in the *Dublin Hospital Reports*.

Graves published many of his lectures in the medical journals of the time; a collection was first published in 1838 in Philadelphia as part of Dunglison's *American Medical Library*. In the same year, the ninth volume of *Zeitschrift fur die Gesamte Medizin*, one of the most successful journals in Germany, was dedicated to him. Five years later, using his lectures as a framework, Graves wrote his *Clinical Lectures on the Practice of Medicine*. This work was a major undertaking of nearly 900 pages and it was dedicated to William Stokes — 'Once his pupil, now his colleague, ever his friend'. The book established his reputation on an international level and was translated into French, German and Italian. Armand Trousseau, the famous French physician, wrote the preface of the French edition in 1862:

> As clinical professor in the Faculty of Medicine in Paris, I have incessantly read and re-read the works of Graves; I have become inspired with it in my teaching; I have endeavoured to imitate it in the book I have myself published on the Clinique of the Hotel Dieu; and even now, although I have almost by heart all the Dublin Professor has written, I cannot refrain from perusing a book which never leaves my study.[17]

It was Trousseau who first proposed that exophthalmic goitre should be known as Graves' Disease.

4.1 Whitley Stokes (1763-1845)

A *physician and scholar, Whitley Stokes worked tirelessly for the poor. The motto of his English-Irish dictionary read:*

> Airgead ná ór ní bhfuil agamsa
> Ach an ní atá bheirim dhibh.

> Silver or gold I have not got
> But that which I have I bring to you.

CHAPTER 4

Stokes: Father and Son

One of Graves' allies in carrying out reforms during his early years in the Meath Hospital was an older physician named Whitley Stokes. He was the first of a long line of doctors in a family which, like the Graves family, has produced leaders in many different areas of endeavour for over three hundred years. One of his descendants, Dr Barbara Stokes, is currently a distinguished paediatrician in Dublin. Adrian Stokes was professor of pathology at Guy's Hospital, London, earlier this century; he died from yellow fever in Africa whilst undertaking research on the condition. The Stokes family also made major contributions to mathematics and Sir George Gabriel Stokes, a cousin of Whitley Stokes, became Lucasian professor of mathematics at Cambridge. In 1845 and 1850 he wrote two papers which created the modern theory on the motion of viscous fluids and he was awarded the Rumford medal by the Royal Society for his discovery of the nature of fluorescence.

Whitley Stokes was born in Waterford in 1763 and received his medical education in Trinity College and Edinburgh. He developed a close friendship with the Irish revolutionary Wolfe Tone, but although he shared many of the ideals of the United Irishmen he began to distance himself from them when he realised that they were preparing for armed rebellion. Despite this, Wolfe Tone still thought very highly of him:

> I love Stokes most sincerely. With a most excellent and highly cultivated mind he possesses the distinguishing characteristic of the best and most feeling heart, and I am sure that it will not hurt the self-love of any of the friends whose names I have recorded when I say in the full force of the phrase, that I look upon Whitley Stokes as the very best man I have ever known.[1]

Although Whitley Stokes' career suffered a setback because he identified so closely with the leaders of the unsuccessful rebellion of 1798, his manifest ability in so many different areas soon opened new opportunities for him. In 1816 he was appointed lecturer of natural history in Trinity College. He was a pioneer in the area of geology and meteorology and made a number of original contributions in these fields, not least in establishing the igneous origin of granite. It was he who first suggested the establishment of the Dublin Zoological Gardens and he was also very involved in planning the Botanic Gardens.

Whitley Stokes joined the staff of the Meath hospital as physician in 1818. The following year he succeeded John Cheyne as professor of medicine in the Royal College of Surgeons and he subsequently became regius professor of physic in the School of Physic. Rather than concentrating on private practice he devoted much of his time to giving medical attention to the poor. He provided the surgeons with opportunities to share clinical teaching with the physicians in the Meath Hospital. This was a major departure from the system of professional apartheid which existed before then as the physician considered the surgeon to be of inferior status. It would be several years before the School of Physic would separate the chairs of anatomy and surgery and make a major commitment to the teaching of surgery as a subject in its own right.

Whitley Stokes was a cultured man who not only wrote works on medical subjects such as contagion and respiration, but also wrote poetry. In 1814 he published, at his own expense, an English-Irish dictionary. His home in Harcourt Street was a meeting place for the city's artists, writers and scientists. It was in their company that his second son, William, who was born in 1804, developed many of the interests which would sustain him during what proved to be one of the most brilliant medical careers of the last century.

William Stokes became one of Robert Graves' first students in the Meath Hospital. He subsequently worked in Glasgow for two years, mainly studying chemistry, and then went to Edinburgh where he was greatly influenced by William Alison, the professor of medicine. Alison was a remarkable man as witnessed by this description of Stokes' first conversation with him. Stokes was walking one night through an old part of Edinburgh:

> He observed a crowd at the entrance of a dark passage; he stopped to see what it could mean; he entered a low room filled with sick poor, Professor Alison being seated among them; he watched the scene; a young man evidently suffering from advanced fever stepped forward. Alison said, 'Go to your bed and when I have done here I will come to you!' Young Stokes

then stepped forward and said 'Sir, I will take the poor man to his home'. 'Who are you?' asked Alison. 'One of your pupils; my name is Stokes .... Let me take this poor man home and I will come and tell you how he goes on.' [2]

Thus began a lifelong relationship between the two doctors. Looking back later in life Stokes said of his teacher:

> Alison was the best man I ever knew ... it was my good fortune to be very closely connected with him during my student days in Edinburgh, and to attend him by day and more often far into the night in his visits of mercy to the sick poor of that city, to whom he was for many years physician, friend, and support.[3]

The French physician René Laënnec had introduced the stethoscope at the Necker Hospital in Paris in 1816 and three years later he published his treatise, 'Traité de L'auscultation Médiate'. Stokes was one of the first to appreciate its potential and in 1825, before qualifying, he published a book on the stethoscope which was the first in the English language. The book, which is 226 pages in length and entitled *An Introduction to the Use of the Stethoscope; With its Application to the Diagnosis in Disease of the Thoracic Viscera; Including the Pathology of These Affections*, is well written and can be read today with profit by any medical student. Stokes was ahead of his time in recognising the great value of the stethoscope; many senior physicians ridiculed the instrument as a novelty that would soon be forgotten while one writer described it as 'the brain born fancy of some speculative enthusiast'.

In 1825 Stokes obtained the degree of Doctor of Medicine from the University of Edinburgh. In Dublin Robert Graves was in need of a young colleague to help him to develop bedside teaching; he also wanted someone who was an expert on the use of the stethoscope. In this way the Meath Hospital could move into the forefront of the rapid advances in clinical methodology. Stokes had made a great impression on Graves while he was a student in the Meath and now Graves started to take soundings among his colleagues to see what chances Stokes would have of being elected to the hospital should his father, Whitley Stokes, agree to resign. Graves knew he would need the support of one of the more influential surgeons, William Henry Porter. Porter was a keen exponent of the importance of pathology and was somewhat anxious that the attention given to the study of the stethoscope might distract students from their pathological studies. Graves dined with Porter and reassured him that the use of the stethoscope would actually increase the need for post-mortem studies as it would be necessary to validate the signs elicited with the new instrument. Graves won Porter's support and they decided on a strategy which was ultimately successful. Whitley Stokes resigned and his son was appointed in 1826, much to the satisfaction of Graves who now worked with renewed enthusiasm on the reform of clinical teaching. Senior students were selected as clinical clerks and became more directly involved in the care of the patients. Their function was:

> to take the cases of the patients committed to their charge — to note the symptoms, stethoscopic, as far as they could, and otherwise. The lessons in the use of the instrument they had been receiving from him for some time previously, enabled them to discharge these duties pretty well. The history, diet and treatment were all accurately noted. The case was read out at the bedside of the patient in the morning before the assembled students. The physician then examined the patient, and if his views did not coincide with the written report, he stated it aloud, and mentioned where the difference lay, and explained how one sound through the stethoscope could be mistaken for another, etc. The physician and student then made a careful examination, and the former instructed the latter where he had misunderstood the signs. The diseased condition of the affected tissue was described, and the remedies to restore its healthy state, or relieve its present distress, decided upon, and the rationale of its action carefully explained.[4]

Stokes was twenty-two when he joined the twenty-nine year old Graves as a physician in the Meath. A close friendship developed between the two men and they immediately began to collaborate on their shared ambition of putting Dublin on the international map of medicine. Stokes placed great emphasis on the importance of original work:

> For it is with societies of men as with individuals, that which earns and extends respect does not depend so much on the teaching of what is already known, no matter how excellent that teaching may be, as upon the productiveness of the society or the individual, of original work.[5]

Graves and Stokes worked together on the new science of auscultation. Richard Townsend, who was associated with the House of Industry Hospitals (Richmond Hospital), was another doctor who shared the enthusiasm of Graves and Stokes for the stethoscope. Like Stokes, he had also been one of the first students to benefit from Graves' teaching in the Meath. He then went to Paris to study under Laënnec where he became convinced that auscultation would revolutionise the practice of medicine. When Townsend returned to Ireland he was invited by John Cheyne, who was then physician general to the forces in Ireland, to examine a patient in

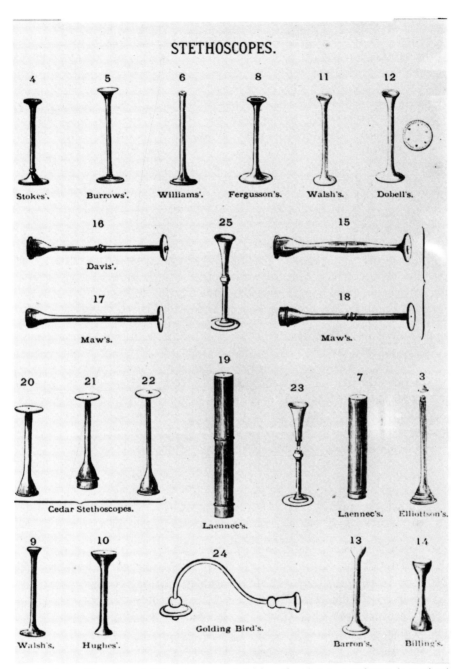

STETHOSCOPES.

4.2 Catalogue illustration of different types of stethoscope (1869)

Included are the early Laënnec stethoscopes (7 & 19) and Stokes' stethoscope (4)

the Royal Hospital Kilmainham. On 25 March 1827 he saw the patient, a tall, well-proportioned dragoon, aged thirty years, and he diagnosed the presence of a tubercular cavity in the upper lobe of the left lung, and a right-sided pneumothorax due to a communication between the bronchus and the pleura. Cheyne was given this diagnosis and a few days later Townsend examined the patient again. This time he detected a pleural effusion. Graves was also invited to listen to the sounds and he expressed surprise at their distinct quality. He thought the resonant sounds which followed coughing were like the tones of a musical snuff box. The patient died on 14 April and Cheyne attended the post mortem. Cheyne was very impressed when he discovered that the findings confirmed the diagnosis made by Townsend with the stethoscope.

Stokes once said that his father left him one legacy: 'the blessed gift of rising early'. He often rose at four or five and worked steadily at writing until eight, when he had breakfast and then began his clinical duties. Stokes gave his first lecture at the Meath Hospital in April 1826. He approached the occasion with some nervousness:

> On the night before my first lecture I sat up until past three in the morning transcribing what I had prepared. I did not finish the task, as, from sheer fatigue both of mind and body, I was obliged to relinquish it. At six in the morning however I sprang from my bed and recommenced my labours, which I finished before breakfast. When the hour came crowds began to pour into the great theatre where I was to make my debut. I found myself quite composed, though as I ascended the stairs an excellent fellow, who had all along shown the greatest anxiety about my success said, 'Stokes my dear fellow, you had better take a pinch of snuff, you look rather pale'.[6]

In 1827 Graves and Stokes wrote a short book entitled *Clinical Reports of the Medical Cases in the Meath Hospital*, based on their early studies in the hospital. They wrote the book primarily for their students and dedicated it to John Cheyne. Stokes gave two lectures on the use of the stethoscope to his students and these were published in 1828. He ended the second lecture by remarking:

> Gentlemen, my colleague and I reflect with pride and pleasure, that in this hospital the stethoscope was first taught in Dublin. In our wards we have diligently used it, not after the manner of empirics to the exclusion of every other method of inquiry; but as a powerful assistant in our diagnosis of disease. From these wards we have sent many accomplished stethoscopists, and we should wish you all to become the same.[7]

In the autumn and winter of 1826, shortly after Stokes had taken up duty in the Meath Hospital, there was a severe epidemic of typhus in Dublin. Stokes wrote a graphic account of the efforts made at the hospital to cope with the problem:

> So widely spread was the epidemic that we were obliged to have additional accommodation for patients provided. Sheds were built, canvas tents were erected, their floors covered with hay, on which the crowds of patients conveyed to the hospital in carts were literally spilled out. I have seen as many as ten patients lying on the hay waiting their turn to be attended to. So immense was the number of sufferers that it became impossible to bestow medical care upon them all.[8]

The Meath Hospital accommodated 300 fever patients and the government made accommodation available for a further 1100 patients. However, this was still not enough and people were dying in the streets. Stokes was horrified and wondered why any person who could afford to leave should opt to stay in what he termed 'this land of poverty and misrule'. He has left us a description of his own experiences during this period:

> I walked out the other night, and in passing by a house my attention was arrested by a crowd of persons gathered in a circle round a group which occupied the steps of a hall door. This was a family consisting of a father, mother, and three wretched children who had been expelled from their lodgings as having fever. The father was in high delirium, and as I approached him he started off and ran down the street; the mother was lying at the foot of the door perfectly insensible, with an infant screaming on the breast, whence it had sought milk in vain; and the other two filled the air with their lamentations. It was a shocking sight indeed. No one would go near them to bring even a drop of cold water. In a short time, however, I succeeded in having them all carried to the hospital where they have since recovered.[9]

Napoleon's famous surgeon, Dominique Jean Larrey, visited Dublin in 1826 with his son. Although he was impressed by the hospitals and medical developments, he was appalled by the poverty and destitution of the people. The typhoid epidemic was raging at the time and he became worried about the safety of his child:

> It is a remarkable contrast to see at all seasons so many individuals, scantily covered by black and tattered rags, and with heads and feet bare, searching the corners of the streets like animals for decaying remains of food, and often hustled by the carriages of the rich, who in this respect show no consideration for these unfortunates .... I longed to get away from this great

city, although we had as it were only glimpsed it; the heart rending picture of these unfortunate people and their maladies had so depressed me that I could not have endured a longer stay.[10]

It was also a time of considerable political upheaval in the country with the great politician Daniel O'Connell leading the agitation for Catholic emancipation. Stokes, like his father, supported the Catholic demands for civil rights but he never became actively involved in politics:

'To me' he wrote 'the real patriot is he who, in a life of labour and of trial, with integrity, practical wisdom, and far-seeing intelligence, labours onward to no other end but that his country shall rise, and with the honourable and justifiable ambition that, loving her, he may rise with her also'.[11]

In January 1829 Stokes wrote to his wife Mary, whom he had met in Glasgow, describing the great political unrest in the country:

that we could all unite in striving for civil and religious liberty that this fair and lovely land, for which God has done so much and man so little, might put forth its smothered energies which now burst forth only to ruin and destroy.[12]

Catholic emancipation was granted in 1829. The Catholic leaders then went on to advocate the repeal of the Act of Union which united Britain and Ireland. Stokes did not show any sympathy for this movement. After the suppression of the Association for the Repeal of the Union in 1830 there was again considerable political unrest. Stokes recorded in February 1831 that the medical students

are divided into two very furious parties. As Dr Jacob was about to commence his lecture the other day he found a placard on the Repeal lying on his table; he took no notice of it but the class began to make a great disturbance, clapping and shouting, etc, so he took up the placard and carried it coolly to the other end of the table where he placed it beneath a large skull. Tranquillity was then restored until the end of the lecture when the confusion recommenced. He held up his hand to obtain silence, then with his peculiar tone and gesture said 'God help you all', and left the room! [13]

CHAPTER 5

Surgeon Anatomists

The most famous Irish surgeon of the last century, Abraham Colles, was born in Kilkenny in 1773 and received his early education at Kilkenny College, a school renowned for its famous pupils including the philosopher George Berkeley, the writer Jonathan Swift, and William Congreve, the dramatist. In September 1790 he entered Trinity College Dublin and at the same time became an apprentice to Philip Woodroffe, surgeon at Dr Steevens' Hospital and the Dublin Foundling Hospital. He also became a registered pupil of the Royal College of Surgeons. Apprenticeship at that time was the recognised way of receiving surgical training. Apart from being a matter of prestige to have apprentices, the surgeon collected substantial fees — minimum fees were £200 if resident or £100 if non-resident but sums of £300-500 were not uncommon.

Colles left for Edinburgh in September 1795, a time when the medical school there was at the height of its fame and medical students were descending on the city from all over the world, particularly from Ireland. The medical school was a very exciting place and at that time was notorious for 'a singularly pugnacious professoriate, who abused one another in a manner which for audacity if not for bitterness would be well-nigh impossible at the present day'.[1] In 1797 Colles graduated with an MD degree. This was the basic degree of Edinburgh at the time, as opposed to the MB degree of Dublin University, and was probably another reason why Edinburgh attracted so many Irish students. Qualification in Dublin was also significantly more expensive as medical students at Trinity College had first to take a BA degree.

Colles spent a few months in London before returning to Dublin. When his former teacher, Philip Woodroffe, died in 1799 Colles was appointed to succeed him as resident surgeon in Dr Steevens' Hospital. In 1804 his academic ability was recognised when he was appointed to the chair of anatomy and physiology in Dr Steevens' and to the chair of surgery in the College of Surgeons.

Colles soon drew large crowds to his lectures and in 1811 he published A *Treatise on Surgical Anatomy*. This book earned him several eponyms in the years following its publication, including Colles' Fascia in the perineum and Colles' Ligament in the inguinal area. Doctors came from all over the world to see Colles operate at Dr Steevens' Hospital.

In 1814 Colles wrote his classical paper on the fracture of the wrist, now known as Colles' Fracture. This paper was published in the *Edinburgh Medical and Surgical Journal*:

> The injury to which I wish to direct the attention of surgeons has not as far as I am aware been described by any author; indeed the form of the carpal extremity of the radius would rather incline us to question its being liable to fracture.[2]

Colles did not gain immediate recognition for his description. His work was later rescued from oblivion by another Dublin surgeon Robert Smith in his *Treatise on Fractures in the Vicinity of the Joints* which was published in 1847. When describing the fracture Smith remarked:

> It is certainly very extraordinary that although the pathology and treatment of this injury were fully and accurately described by Mr Colles so long back as April 1814 not a single British or foreign author who has written since has made the slightest reference to Mr Colles' name in connection with the subject, even when almost quoting his words.[3]

Because of its association with Colles and his successor as resident surgeon, James Cusack, Dr Steevens' Hospital acquired the reputation of being the leading surgical hospital in the city. However, the hospital also had able physicians such as Sir Henry Marsh who was a graduate of Trinity College. He had initially hoped to practise surgery but in 1818 he received a wound while dissecting in the College of Surgeons, which resulted in the amputation of his right forefinger. He then decided to become a physician and spent the greater part of 1819 and 1820 on the Continent, chiefly in the Hospital La Charitè in Paris. He became professor of medicine in the Park Street School and in the College of Surgeons. Marsh lectured on diseases of children and he was a founder of the Institute for Sick Children in Pitt Street (now Balfe Street). The National Children's Hospital in Harcourt Street is the direct descendant of this institute. Marsh was one of the first six founder presidents of the Pathological Society of Dublin. He was elected to the presidency

From Kirkpatrick's *History of Dr Steevens' Hospital* (1924)

5.1   Abraham Colles (1773-1843)

Colles was the most famous surgeon of the Irish school and his reputation helped attract students to Dublin. A fluent speaker, he enlivened his lectures with practical anecdotes and humorous stories which sent his large classes into roars of laughter.

of the Royal College of Physicians in 1841 and his statue, executed by the sculptor J H Foley, stands in the hall of the College of Physicians in Kildare Street, together with those of Corrigan, Graves and Stokes.

Colles retired from the chair of surgery in 1836, just a year before the publication of his most famous book *Practical Observations on the Venereal Diseases and on the Use of Mercury*. In those pre-antibiotic days the treatment of syphilis, which could cause horrible deformities, was a major problem. Mercury had been used as a treatment for the condition for many centuries. One of the effects of the drug was to stimulate the production of saliva, and physicians and surgeons judged the efficacy of the treatment by the amount of saliva produced. Large pewter mugs were kept in Dr Steevens' Hospital for the patients to spit into, and the dose of mercury was adjusted depending on the number of mugs filled during the day. Huge doses were frequently used and the side effects of the therapy were often worse than those of the disease being treated. Abraham Colles believed strongly in the efficacy of mercury treatment but he maintained that the best results were obtained with small doses of the agent. This recommendation was based on his clinical observations and its wide adoption saved many from the excesses of treatment. However there were others such as Richard Carmichael, a surgeon at the Richmond Hospital, who thought that mercury should not be used in the treatment of syphilis because of its side effects. Carmichael was one of those who reviewed Abraham Colles' book on venereal disease:

> I know how strongly he is wedded to early opinions and associations, and that I might as well attempt to shake a pious Mussulman from his faith, that there is no God but Allah, and that Mahomed is his prophet, as to endeavour to dissuade my friend from his belief in the infallible powers of mercury ... a belief which may aptly be parodied ... to overcome the malady there is no God but mercury, and Abraham is his prophet.[4]

At the time of its publication Colles' book received a very unfavourable review in *The Lancet*. Over the previous years *The Lancet* had been publishing lectures on venereal disease by another Dublin doctor, William Wallace. After condemning the book as containing nothing original, the reviewer finished with the observation that 'Dr Colles has taken especial care to keep from the public eye, in his pages, the names both of Carmichael and Wallace, brethren residing in the same city, highly appreciated there, and well known wherever British medical literature has reached, as distinguished contributors to our knowledge of venereal diseases'.[5]

William Wallace was a surgeon attached to the Charitable Infirmary, Jervis Street. In 1818 he also established at his own expense a hospital for

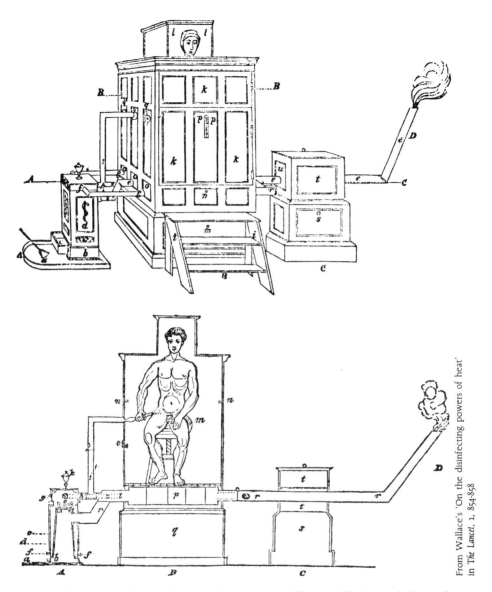

From Wallace's 'On the disinfecting powers of heat' in *The Lancet*, 1, 854-858

5.2 (a) & (b) Apparatus for disinfection and fumigation used at the Dublin Infirmary for the treatment of cutaneous diseases

Wallace used 'the power of heated air and of many other agents to destroy contagion'. The apparatus consisted of a furnace (A), a compartment for the patient or material to be fumigated (B), and a second smaller compartment (C) 'to heat the patient's clothes and the sheets which are to be put around him when he comes out of the apparatus'. Wallace used it primarily for patients with cowpox, smallpox and syphilis.

skin diseases in Moore Street and according to the medical historian, Cameron, it was the first of its kind in Ireland and Great Britain. His book on venereal disease, which was published in 1833, contained the first description of lymphogranuloma venereum, a sexually transmitted infection caused by small intra-cellular bacteria known as Chlamydia. He demonstrated the contagious nature of secondary syphilis, which manifests itself about six weeks after the initial local lesion has healed if the latter has not been treated adequately. Among other symptoms, the patient develops a generalised rash and swelling of the lymph glands. Wallace introduced potassium iodide as a treatment for syphilis and this agent was used until more effective treatments were developed earlier this century. Pusey, in his *History of Syphilis*, describes this as 'the most important contribution' to the treatment of syphilis in the nineteenth century. However, even though Wallace made significant contributions to the contemporary knowledge of venereal disease, many of his experiments were unjustifiable. For instance, he inoculated healthy subjects with the discharge from syphilitic lesions in order to prove that the secondary form of the disease was contagious. According to Cameron, the nature of these experiments, which were published in *The Lancet* in 1837, had not been explained to the subjects beforehand. Wallace gave the following description of his technique, showing how he transferred the discharge from the patient (MD) to the healthy subject (PK):

> Having by friction with the end of my finger, covered with a towel, removed the cuticle to the extent of the size of a shilling from the anterior and inner part of the right thigh of PK, a very healthy-looking person, aged 19 years, a raw surface was formed, which oozed blood. To this surface I applied a piece of lint moistened in the discharge of the diseased patches of MD.[6]

Wallace faithfully recorded the changes on PK's thigh, and two months later he was able to write:

> The characters of the sore on the thigh are more marked, its base is harder: its centre more depressed: its fungous rim is raised considerably higher than the surrounding skin, and its discharge which has a dirty-brown colour is more copious. He complains of a stiffness extending along his thigh from the rubbed surface to the groin, the glands of which are swelled but not inflamed.[6]

The subject also developed generalised symptoms. These symptoms and the local lesion gradually responded to mercury treatment. Wallace was very pleased:

Can any experiment be more satisfactory? It strongly illustrates the contagious character of the secretions of the diseased patches of MD .... Lastly it testifies to the beneficial action of mercury in this form of disease, whether locally or constitutionally employed.[6]

Wallace was a frequent contributor to the early volumes of The Lancet. In 1837 he contributed three papers on 'The structure of the Negro's skin'. This work was based on experiments which he had carried out on the skin of Nicholls, a black man from St Domingo whom Wallace kept in his house for the purpose of his research.

Wallace died from typhus a short time after the publication of these papers and The Lancet noticed his demise with regret:

Dr Wallace was an old and able contributor to the advancement of medical science in the pages of this Journal.... The fever which attacked him while in attendance on some poor patients, terminated fatally within a few days. We must lament the loss of a friend, but our sorrow is tempered by the recollection that he has perished a martyr in the righteous cause of humanity.[7]

Colles had resigned the chair of surgery because ill health had made it difficult for him to fulfil all his duties. He had frequent attacks of gout and suffered from troublesome breathlessness. He was seen in 1840 by William Stokes, who found on examination that 'the impulses were feeble, irregular and rapid, and the organ seemed to impinge against a surface larger than natural; the action of the heart was at times so irregular and rapid, that it was with great difficulty the sounds could be analysed'.[8] Colles was advised to resign his hospital appointment and to travel to Switzerland. On his return his condition deteriorated and he wondered if he had valvular heart disease and not as Stokes had thought bronchitis and a dilated heart. Before his death he asked Stokes to arrange a post-mortem examination of his body, to be carried out by Robert Smith. He thought it would be of benefit 'to ascertain by examination the exact seat and nature of my last disease. The parts to which I would direct particular attention are the heart and lungs, a small hernia immediately above the umbilicus, and the swelling in the right hypochondrium'.[9]

Colles died in 1843 and the post mortem was performed as requested. The findings revealed a fibrotic left lung and a dilated heart without valvular disease. On 9 December 1843 Robert Smith communicated his findings to the Pathological Society of Dublin.

Colles trained a number of men who subsequently became outstanding anatomists and surgeons, including the anatomist Benjamin Alcock, the eye surgeon Arthur Jacob, and the eye and ear surgeon William Wilde. Benjamin Alcock began his studies under Macartney and was indentured to Abraham Colles in 1819. He was also from Kilkenny and Colles described him as 'an intelligent and active young man, one whom I have known to have studied his profession very diligently and with the most ample opportunities'. He was the first to describe the Pudendal Canal (Alcock's Canal). The description appeared in *The Cyclopaedia of Anatomy and Physiology*, a prestigious work in six volumes, which was edited by Robert B Todd and published in London between 1835 and 1839. Todd was the son of Charles H Todd, professor of surgery in the Royal College of Surgeons in Ireland. After studying in the Royal College of Surgeons Robert Todd went to London where he had a brilliant career. He was a founder of King's College Hospital, London, and he described the temporary paralysis which may follow an epileptic attack, known today as Todd's Paralysis.

After a period of teaching in some of the private medical schools, including the Park Street School and the Apothecaries' Hall, Cecilia Street, Alcock left Dublin in 1849 to become the first professor of anatomy in Queen's College Cork (now University College Cork). However, his time in Cork was full of acrimony and he had several very serious disputes with the president, Robert Kane. He was dismissed from his post in 1855 and a few years later he emigrated to America. Nothing is known about his subsequent career there.

Arthur Jacob was born in 1790 near Maryborough, now known as Portlaoise, and both his father and grandfather were doctors. Having obtained his surgical diploma at the College of Surgeons he went to Edinburgh where he graduated with an MD degree in 1813 at the age of twenty-three. He subsequently studied in London and Paris but his postgraduate tour was halted by the political upheaval caused by Napoleon's escape from Elba.

When Jacob returned to Dublin, Macartney invited him to lecture on the anatomy, physiology and pathology of the eye and to assist him at a dispensary which he had opened in 1814 for skin and eye problems. Macartney had an interest in eye disease and had studied the anatomy of the eye in mammals. Jacob continued this work under the professor's direction. His research was rewarded in 1819 when he published a paper describing his discovery of the bacillary layer or the layer of rods and cones in the eye. This became known as Jacob's Membrane and is the light-sensitive layer of the retina. Jacob wrote:

5.3 Arthur Jacob (1790-1874)

He was the first to describe the neural layer of the retina. He was also a founder member of the Royal City of Dublin Hospital (1832). The Dublin Medical Press which he established in 1839 survived in London until 1961 as the Medical Press and Circular.

I find that the retina is covered on its external surface by a delicate transparent membrane united to it by cellular substance and vessels. This structure, not hitherto noticed by anatomists, I first observed in the spring of the last year and have since so frequently demonstrated, as to leave no doubt on my mind of its existence as a distinct and perfect membrane.[10]

In 1827 Jacob also described 'an ulcer of peculiar character which attacks the eyelids and other parts of the face'. This ulcer, known as Jacob's Ulcer in the last century, is now called a rodent ulcer. Jacob was proud of his description and he never failed to draw it to the attention of subsequent authors who failed to acknowledge his work. Time has added little to the accuracy of his original description:

The characteristic features of this disease are the slowness of its progress, the peculiar condition of the edges and surface of the ulcer, the comparatively inconsiderable suffering produced by it, its incurable nature unless by extirpation, and its not contaminating the neighbouring lymphatic glands.[11]

Eye surgery like other surgery was very crude at the time. Jacob treated cataract by a method known as 'needling'. Rather than remove the cataract, he inserted a needle into the opaque lens, breaking it up into small parts which were gradually absorbed over a period of weeks. He dismissed as malicious the claim that he favoured needling simply because he was not skilled enough to remove the cataract and he maintained that cataract extraction was much more dangerous. He used a domestic sewing needle which he bent at the point to fragment the cataract. Jacob described his technique as follows:

When he is seated I lay the patient's head against my chest, and placing the middle finger of my left hand on his lower and the forefinger on his upper eyelid, and gently holding the eye between them, I strike the point of the needle suddenly into the cornea, about a line from its margin, and there hold it until any struggles of the patient, which may be made, cease. There must be no hesitation here, for if the cornea be touched without fixing the point of the needle in it, the eye will turn rapidly and the surface will be scratched. I advise the operator to pause here for a moment, holding the eye firmly and steadily on the point of his needle, and if necessary to say a word of encouragement or remonstrance to the patient.[12]

Jacob was appointed professor of anatomy and physiology at the College of Surgeons in 1826 and filled the post for forty-one years. Cameron, the historian of the College of Surgeons, has left us this description of him:

As a writer he was much given to drastic polemical articles which frequently irritated those against whom they were directed. He rarely indulged in even the mildest festivities, but devoted himself wholly to his professional and editorial work and to original research. He remained up till after midnight as a rule, nevertheless he was always punctually at work early in the day. He had an intense dislike of charlatanism and humbug of every kind. He took a deep interest in the success of his pupils and he laboured hard to instruct them. One of his few weaknesses was his notion that he alone of the professors should always give the introductory lecture at the commencement of the session at the College School.[13]

Jacob was one of the surgeons involved with Graves in establishing the private medical school in Park Street. For a short period he also joined Graves and Stokes to edit the *Dublin Journal of Medical Science*, which had been established originally as the *Dublin Journal of Medical and Chemical Science* by Robert Kane in 1832. Kane had worked as a medical student under both Graves and Stokes and was professor of chemistry at the Apothecaries' Hall in Cecilia Street. He was destined to lead a very brilliant career and became the first president of Queen's College Cork in 1849. After the first two or three issues were published Graves and Stokes joined Kane as editors of the journal and two years later Kane resigned on becoming professor of natural philosophy to the Royal Dublin Society. Stokes and Graves continued to edit the journal until 1842. This journal provided a forum for the work of Irish doctors and it brought their achievements to the attention of colleagues in other countries. It also kept its readers abreast of the latest advances on the Continent. The journal is still published today as the *Irish Journal of Medical Science*.

Jacob became an assistant editor in 1836 but his approach was considered too controversial and his connection with the journal was discontinued. This may explain why he published a very bitter attack on Graves a few years later in the *Dublin Medical Press*, a journal which Jacob established in 1839 in collaboration with Henry Maunsell, professor of midwifery in the College of Surgeons. Graves, in discussing the therapeutic uses of mercury, had emphasised the need for caution in its use and had made some remarks which, in the opinion of the leader writer in the *Dublin Medical Press*, reflected on the competence of the rank and file of the profession. In an editorial entitled 'Scratch me, and I'll Scratch You' Graves' opinions were dismissed as 'the chronic medico literary diarrhoea under which the learned professor has so long laboured' and as 'heterogeneous discharges with which he inundates the journals'. Graves was aware that many doctors harmed their patients at the time by inappropriate prescribing and by the excessive use of remedies such as bleeding and purging. During his first lecture at the Meath Hospital he told his students that licensed practitioners gave as much poison to their patients as the quacks who 'cover our walls with their advertisements'.[14]

CHAPTER 6

From Feeding Fevers to
Foetal Heartbeats:
New Insights in Medicine

In 1832 there was a mysterious death in the seaport of Dun Laoghaire, just south of Dublin. Stokes and another doctor named Rumley, who later became president of the Royal College of Surgeons, were asked to investigate the death. Both doctors agreed that it was a case of Asiatic cholera, although they had never seen an instance of it before. Over the previous few years the disease had been making its way across Europe. As early as 1826 Graves had predicted that it was only a matter of time before it would reach Ireland. A crowd waited outside the dead man's house and when they were told the cause of the death their initial reaction of dismay gradually turned to fury. A mob of men and women attacked the doctors' carriage and they were lucky to get away unharmed. The outbreak of the disease in other parts of Ireland, within a short period of time, confirmed the accuracy of the diagnosis.

Treating patients with such potentially lethal diseases required considerable courage on the part of the doctors. Many of them died, and many others including Graves were lucky to survive. In later life Stokes recalled how Rumley had begun to complain of some of the symptoms associated with cholera as they were both on their way back to Dublin after seeing the first victim. Rumley's symptoms, which included abdominal cramp and a feeling of imminent death, lasted for a few days. Soon the city was in the grip of the epidemic and Rumley, having come to the conclusion that his own symptoms were imaginary, decided that he should do something to steel his nerves if he was to play a useful role in treating the victims. He volunteered his services to a crowded temporary cholera hospital where he remained for thirty-six hours in close attendance on the sick. During the first eighteen hours seven of the patients he was attending died. His own preoccupations were rapidly cured by this horrific reality.

Cholera was only one of the many infectious diseases which killed nurses, medical students and doctors at the time. Many young surgeons died as a result of overwhelming infection following accidental cuts on the hand whilst performing operations or post mortems. Stokes nearly died in 1827 when he developed an overwhelming infection as a result of a cut on his hand received while dissecting. This incident was followed very quickly by another serious illness, typhus, which almost proved fatal.

Graves devoted much of his attention to the problems of fever patients and he revolutionised their treatment by stressing the importance of adequate nourishment. Up to then fever patients had been placed on a very spartan diet. 'You are not' he told his students, 'to permit your patient to encounter the terrible consequences of starvation because he does not ask for nutriment'. One day whilst on his ward round he noted the healthy appearance of some patients who had recovered from severe typhus. 'This is all the effect of our good feeding' he exclaimed 'and lest when I am gone you may be at a loss for an epitaph for me, let me give you one, in three words — He Fed Fevers!'.

Around this time students began to arrive from England in significant numbers to study under Graves and Stokes. Thomas Fitzpatrick, a pupil who came to study at the hospital in 1830, later recalled:

> We had then in the Meath Hospital a most numerous class of English students; perhaps there has not been so large a class in that hospital since. The result was that we Irishmen were stimulated to work in a way that Dr Stokes told me he had never seen equalled. We were stimulated first by the establishment of premiums, and next by the energy of the Englishmen.[1]

Some of these English students were non-conformists who wished to become fellows of the Royal College of Physicians of London; an indispensable qualification for this however was the possession of a degree from Oxford, Cambridge or Dublin. As non-conformists were barred from taking degrees at the two former colleges they came instead to Trinity College.

In 1831 Graves and Stokes decided to award prizes to the most competent students. Emphasis was placed on the following criteria when deciding on the distribution of the prizes:

1. The writing of the best reports, with clinical and general observation on the cases taken.
2. The length of time the candidate had practised on the wards.
3. His diligence and general conduct.

At 9 am on Monday 2 May 1831 Graves and Stokes met the students in the hospital lecture theatre for the inauguration of the prizes. The fact that the occasion was reported in the *London Medical Gazette* three weeks later (31 May) is an indication of the growing importance of the hospital as a teaching centre. The case presentations were discussed by both Graves and Stokes and they ranged over a wide spectrum of diseases including aneurysm of the aorta, bronchitis, hemiplegia, epilepsy, disease of the mitral valves, brain abscess, jaundice, delirium tremens, meningitis, diphtheria, abdominal tumour and pericarditis. The names of the winners were announced and the ceremony concluded with the prize-giving.

Stokes was very proud of the clinical teaching in the Meath Hospital which fostered self-education and self-reliance by making the student responsible for the care of individual patients. He was very much against cramming students with facts:

> His great object in teaching medicine was to make his pupils practical men, to stimulate them to original investigation, and to make them feel that he himself was in all cases their fellow student.[2]

He appreciated the importance of constantly renewing and revitalising lectures, believing, like Matthew Arnold, that the lecturer should 'not supply his hearers from a cistern but give them living water'. In order to do this, Stokes believed that the teacher must also be involved in research:

> He cannot expect to command attention or interest when he gives, year after year, only the same facts, views and arguments, no matter how valuable they may be. For even to those who hear him for the first time, his discourse will fail in vitality, and in producing that sympathy between the speaker and the hearer, which makes the latter not only receive gladly what has been said, but almost anticipate that which is to follow. This power is attainable only when the teacher is himself an original investigator, when he has himself been permitted to strike the rock, and to cause it to pour forth the fresh and sparkling stream.[3]

Stokes' lectures at the Meath Hospital and the Park Street School attracted considerable attention. They were published over several volumes in the *London Medical and Surgical Journal*. They were subsequently edited by a Dr John Bell and published in Philadelphia in 1840 under the title *Clinical Lectures on the Theory and Practice of Medicine*. This book was for many years a textbook in the American schools of medicine. In his preface Bell wrote:

> One, and not the least of the merits of the Irish School of Medicine, so ably represented on this occasion by Dr Stokes, is in its large and judicious

borrowing from the French discoveries in morbid anatomy, and in combining the deductions which they supply with Hippocratic observation of symptoms and the externals of disease, so as to form a harmonious body of doctrine of general pathology and diagnosis.[4]

This book made the new methods of clinical examination accessible to a large medical public.

In 1835 Stokes began writing his major work on thoracic disease, but within a year his health showed signs of breaking down. He was subject to bouts of depression and severe headaches which disabled him for days. He was persuaded eventually to take a month off to travel in Europe. His book *On the Diagnosis and Treatment of Diseases of the Chest* was published in 1837 and within a year it was translated into German and published in Bremen by Dr Gerhard Von dem Busch. In his preface Von dem Busch wrote: 'Since the publication of Laënnec's great work, which formed an epoch in medical history, many valuable treatises have appeared in France and England on the same subject, but none of them can bear comparison with that which has lately emanated from the pen of Dr William Stokes.'

In this work Stokes made several original contributions to medicine, including his discovery of a stage of pneumonia prior to that described by Laënnec as the first. He also reported his use of the stethoscope as an aid to the detection of foreign bodies in the air passages. The book brought the clinical methods of the Dublin physicians to the attention of a wide readership and, in particular, helped to disseminate the advances which had been made in the diagnosis of chest conditions with the use of the stethoscope. The book was reviewed by Dominic Corrigan, who had been a student with Stokes in Edinburgh, for the *Dublin Journal of Medical Science*. He wrote that it would be 'hailed with delight both by those who see their profession as a science, and by those who more humbly but not less usefully cultivate it as a practical art, seeking in each new page that is presented to them the means of curing or alleviating disease'.[5]

John Creery Ferguson was another member of the Dublin school of medicine whose fame was associated with the use of the stethoscope. Born in 1802, his father was an apothecary in County Armagh. Having won an entrance scholarship to Trinity he also won the gold medal, as he was placed first in the examination. He obtained a BA degree in 1823 and a year later he travelled with Stokes to Edinburgh for further experience. He graduated in medicine from Edinburgh in 1825, along with Stokes and Corrigan. Ferguson was to become the first doctor in Ireland and Great Britain to hear the foetal heart.

Ferguson kept a diary which he began on the day he left Dublin with Stokes to board the boat at Belfast: 'October, 30th, 1824 was spent, the weather being remarkably fine, on the day Mail by your humble servant accompanied by his friend Stokes, rather agreeably, save when a casual cloud lowered emanating from the recollections of those we left behind us.'[6] They eventually arrived in Edinburgh and Ferguson made the following entry in his diary on 12 November:

> Immediately after breakfast called on Dr Alison to gain some information from him in relation to graduating. Found him extremely civil and communicative. Find I have all the necessaries for a degree and may do what I please. Enjoyed some general conversation with him. Introduced by Stokes to Dr Cullen, a very gentlemanlike young man, who to use his own words 'will introduce us to everyone in Edinburgh worth knowing!' Has a sovereign contempt for the teachers of the old school. Accompanied us to the infirmary and very kindly introduced us to Drs Russell, Balingall and other knobs. What shall I say of the Infirmary? it is so very inferior in every respect, but particularly as a School, to all our Dublin hospitals,

By courtesy of RCSI

6.1 John Creery Ferguson and colleagues (1802-1865)

Ferguson (seated third from the right) is seen here attending a meeting on microscopy. William Wilde is almost certainly the person seated second from the left.

that it needs no remarks. Suffice it to say that students to the number of 295 fight and jostle each other around a patient's bed to have even a view of him or her.[7]

Ferguson spent a year in Edinburgh and appears to have found the city very dull, particularly the strict Scottish Calvinistic Sunday. However, there were some compensations. One evening they heard some dance music coming from the flat underneath and they tried unsuccessfully to join the party. Undeterred, Ferguson recalled:

> On our return from lecture attracted again by music and the dance proceeding in the flat below us, vexed at our disappointment on the former evening and inspired certainly by consummate impudence, we sent down our landlady with our compliments and two handsome Irish lads would most willingly join their revel. No sooner were the glad tidings received than we had a regular invitation ... introduced to the company, admired by all the girls and regularly walked over all the Scotchmen, we spent a very pleasant evening .... This is the first spree I have had since I came to this hole.[8]

They looked forward to mail from Dublin and on one occasion Ferguson 'found a letter in the Post Office for Stokes. Borrowed money from Higgins and paid for it. Brought it home. Happy fellow! Had two letters and a newspaper from Dublin today. Well every dog has his day'. Ten days later the homesick Ferguson had still not received a letter and he wrote despairingly: 'Am I never to hear from home?' He was also running very low in funds: 'My shoemaker has found me without a penny. Oh! poverty, poverty poverty!!!' He had to borrow ten pounds to see him out of his difficulties. However, after another few days a parcel of letters arrived, one of which enclosed 'an order on the Bank for £20 thanks to my worthy old Father .... I am the happiest man in Christendom.'[9]

Ferguson pioneered the use of the stethoscope in diagnosing pregnancy in Ireland and Great Britain. Foetal heart sounds were first heard with the stethoscope by a French physician and colleague of Laënnec named Kergaradec. However, contemporary French obstetricians failed to realise the significance of Kergaradec's work and one elderly obstetrician strongly advised him to 'abandon these toys of ignorance, truly prejudicial to science and the well-being of an amiable and interesting sex'. Ferguson visited Paris where Laënnec and Kergaradec introduced him to auscultation of the pregnant human abdomen. He returned to Ireland convinced of the importance of foetal auscultation and in November 1827, at the Dublin General Dispensary in Temple Bar, he heard the human foetal heart for the first time in these islands. He read a paper 'Auscultation, the only

unequivocal evidence of pregnancy' to the Association of Fellows and
Licentiates of the Irish College of Physicians on 2 November 1828:

> But as a few cases have occurred to me of late, which in no small degree
> interested myself, where pregnancy was most artfully and successfully
> attempted to be concealed, and where the stethoscope alone could give
> unequivocal signs, as might enable a medical man to pronounce, without
> the possibility of error, on the presence of a foetus, I shall offer no apology
> for laying them before the Association.[10]

Ferguson also appreciated the potential of the stethoscope as a means of
confirming that the foetus was alive in cases of known pregnancy. Before
he described his cases he mentioned an observation he had made under
unusual circumstances:

> A goat had been procured for a very different purpose by Doctors Hunt,
> Corrigan and myself, and bound on its back on the operating table. I casually
> applied the stethoscope to the abdomen, without the slightest previous
> knowledge of its pregnancy, and was surprised to detect almost immediately
> the distinct double pulsations of a foetal heart. My two friends, to whose
> accuracy of observation I have been indebted, satisfied themselves perfectly
> of the fact, and on examining the uterus about an hour afterwards, we
> extracted a foetus, of which the minute preparation which I now offer was
> the heart. On enquiring from the person who sold us the goat, on whose
> accuracy we could depend, we learned that it was exactly seven weeks
> from copulation.[10]

One of the cases he described at the meeting was that of a young woman
complaining of indigestion whom he saw three times before suspecting
that she might be pregnant. She denied having any of the signs of pregnancy
and claimed that her abdomen swelled only occasionally. However, when
Ferguson listened with his stethoscope he heard the distinct sounds of the
foetal heart:

> The patient received the news with extreme indignation. Indeed this young
> lady's histrionic talent was of the first order and such was her well-feigned
> agony at the very idea of her virgin innocence being ever suspected that
> had I not positive evidence of my senses to confirm the opinion I had
> expressed I should have felt extremely uncomfortable.[10]

Ferguson recommended the use of the stethoscope to Robert Collins, the
master of the Rotunda, and to his assistants Evory Kennedy and O'Brien
Adams. Unlike the French obstetricians they responded with enthusiasm
and foetal auscultation became routine practice in their wards in the early
1830s. Evory Kennedy published his experiences of foetal auscultation in

1833 in a monograph *Obstetric Auscultation; or Means of Detecting Life or Death of the Foetus before Birth*. This original and comprehensive book made Kennedy a foremost figure in European obstetrics. It had a major influence on the development of Scottish and, much later on, English obstetric theory and practice in relation to the well-being of the foetus.

John Creery Ferguson was elected King's professor of the practice of medicine in the School of Physic in 1846. Four years later he was appointed to the first chair of medicine at Queen's College Belfast.

CHAPTER 7

Corrigan and Adams

Dominic Corrigan was born in 1802 and as a child he lived in Thomas Street, in the heart of the old city of Dublin, where his father was a merchant. By a strange coincidence his father's shop was situated on the site of the medieval hospital of St John the Baptist which had been suppressed by Henry VIII in the sixteenth century. By the end of the eighteenth century some of the more repressive anti-Catholic legislation had been repealed and an ecclesiastical college, St Patrick's, was established at Maynooth in 1795. These developments opened up new opportunities for young Catholics like Corrigan.

Corrigan was educated at a lay college which was linked to the seminary at Maynooth. A member of the staff, Dr Cornelius Denvir, who taught mathematics, physics and chemistry, exerted an important influence on him at this stage and almost certainly laid the foundations for Corrigan's later interest in haemodynamics, including his famous work on malfunction of the aortic valve. Denvir was so impressed by Corrigan's ability that he asked him to prepare the experiments which he used as demonstrations during his lectures. The medical attendant of the college, Dr O'Kelly, was also very impressed by Corrigan's ability and it was at his suggestion that Corrigan first decided to study medicine. Before he left Maynooth, O'Kelly gave him some instruction in medicine and surgery.

Corrigan entered the School of Physic of the University of Dublin in 1820. Here he came under the influence of Macartney, the dynamic professor of anatomy who had also made such a great impact on Graves. Corrigan, like other medical students, took an active part in procuring bodies for dissection as the only legal source of bodies at this time was that of executed criminals and the number supplied in this way was totally inadequate. To remedy this situation the medical schools condoned the practice of body snatching. Bully's Acre, adjacent to the Royal Hospital Kilmainham, was the burial place for paupers and the cemetery usually visited by the body snatchers on their midnight forays. Corrigan had some hair-raising experiences on these expeditions, beginning with his first night when it was his task to open a grave in which a body had recently been interred:

> I worked vigorously, and on reaching the frail coffin had no difficulty in breaking back its upper third; but on stooping down in the usual way, with my head downwards and my feet slanting upwards, I had to support myself by resting my hands on the chest of the dead; when what was my horror to hear a loud prolonged groan from the corpse. I suddenly drew myself upwards, but there was no repetition until I again supported myself on my hands resting on the chest, when another prolonged groan was audible. The cause, on a little examination, became then explicable. The body was an impoverished weakly skeleton, and the pressure of my weight forced the air in the chest up through the trachea and larynx, and produced the sounds which had momentarily terrified me.[1]

On another occasion he was entering the cemetery after midnight with a fellow student when they saw a white object apparently floating around one of the graves which had been marked. They plucked up their courage and approached the grave cautiously. The white object turned out to be the dress of a poor woman 'who was rocking herself to and fro over the grave. She was the widow of the poor man buried beneath, who had died on his way home from working the harvest in England, and the poor woman had remained to watch over his remains. It need scarcely be added, that we pledged ourselves to respect the remains for her sake, that we kept our word, and that we made up a small collection to afford her some aid'.[1]

The middle and upper classes began to join the popular agitation against the practice of body snatching. Macartney's first reaction to this development was rather blunt. He wrote a letter to the newspapers pointing out that these people were not only undermining medical education but that they were also undermining a system by which many of them were supplied with artificial teeth and hair. He cannot have made much progress with this line of argument as in 1828 he adopted a different approach when he drew up and published the following document:

> We whose names are here unto affixed, being convinced that the study of Anatomy is of the utmost value to mankind, in as much as it illustrates various branches of Natural and Moral Science, and constitutes the very

By courtesy of RCPI

7.1 Dominic Corrigan (1802-1880)
On his appointment to the Charitable Infirmary, Jervis Street, Corrigan had only six medical beds. He studied his patients with great diligence and in 1832, whilst still at Jervis Street, he wrote his famous paper on inadequacy of the aortic valves.

59

basis of the healing art; and believing that the erroneous opinions and vulgar prejudices which prevail, with regard to dissections, will be most effectually removed by practical example; do hereby deliberately and solemnly express our desire that, at the usual period after death, our bodies, instead of being interred, should be devoted by our surviving friends to the more rational, benevolent and honourable purpose of explaining the structure, functions and diseases of the human body.[2]

He persuaded ninety-nine leading citizens to sign the document with him. This new spirit and the passing of the Anatomy Act of 1832, which ensured an adequate number of subjects for dissection from various institutions, led to the rapid decline in the practice of body snatching. The Act stipulated strict conditions for anatomical dissection and it allowed those having lawful possession of a body to donate it for anatomical purposes, provided the deceased had not objected during their lifetime and that the next of kin agreed.

Like many other Irish medical students, Corrigan travelled to Edinburgh to complete his medical studies and to take the final examinations. He felt lonely and depressed in the city as he prepared himself for the examiners:

Coming before the professors here a perfect stranger to them, I dreaded they might be more strict, and reasonably so, on me than on one of their pupils. This had at least the effect of making me study much harder than otherwise I might. My examination lasted about two hours, and was I think as fair as if I had studied under themselves. Happening, and indeed principally on account of my intimacy with Mr Denvir, professor of Natural Philosophy in Maynooth, to have been well prepared in chemistry, I answered pretty well on that subject. This pleased the professor of Chemistry here, and (each professor thinking his own branch the most important) when announcing to me the result of the examination, he told me it would be very pleasing to all the professors if all my countrymen came as well prepared before them. I thanked him for the compliment, and never I believe, before thanked a stranger so sincerely, for during the short interval that elapsed between the termination of my examination, and the verdict being made known to me, I suffered anxiety that I would not again experience for any consideration.[3]

Corrigan graduated as a doctor of medicine in 1825. The tremendous influence that Edinburgh had on Irish medicine can be judged from the fact that there were more Irish students than Scottish students graduating in medicine at Edinburgh at that time.

Corrigan's first post in Dublin was as physician to the Sick Poor Institution in Meath Street to which he was appointed in 1826. This was the largest dispensary in the city and, although it was not attached to a hospital, Corrigan had the satisfaction of knowing that the post had once been held by Abraham Colles, the leading Irish surgeon of the period. Two years after this appointment Corrigan published his first paper on auscultation of the heart in *The Lancet*. This was followed by several other papers and his hard work was rewarded in 1831 when he was appointed physician to the Charitable Infirmary in Jervis Street. He performed his clinical duties with great dedication, arriving on the ward every morning at eight o'clock, with a class of students, to attend his patients. This was a practice he followed for many years.

In 1832 Corrigan's classic paper 'On permanent patency of the mouth of the aorta or inadequacy of the aortic valves' appeared in the *Edinburgh Medical and Surgical Journal*. He described the typical signs which are associated with incompetence of the aortic valve, including the pulsation which is seen in the neck. Soon physicians from around the world including Armand Trousseau in Paris began to speak of Corrigan's Disease and the eponym first appeared in print in 1839 in *La Lancette Française*. Corrigan was now at the height of his achievement. In 1834 he moved his residence to No 4 (now 92) Merrion Square, where he joined the élite of his profession. His reputation and practice grew rapidly and for many years he was the most popular and most highly remunerated physician in Dublin. He continued to publish and in 1838 he wrote the first description of chronic fibrosis of the lung. Corrigan also sensed that he was part of a new movement in Irish medicine. When speaking at the opening session of the Dublin Medico-Chirurgical Society in 1837 he remarked:

> The Irish School of Medicine and Surgery is, if I am not mistaken, exerting a silent but deeply spreading influence upon society, an influence which is beneficial, and which will I hope be lasting.[4]

In 1837 Corrigan was appointed physician to the Cork Street Fever Hospital and three years later he joined the staff of the House of Industry Hospitals. These hospitals were associated with the Dublin House of Industry which was established in 1772. They consisted of the Hardwicke (fever), Richmond (surgical) and Whitworth (medical) hospitals but the group was known colloquially as the Richmond Hospital. In moving from the Charitable Infirmary to the Richmond Hospital, Corrigan was following in the footsteps of a colleague, the surgeon Robert Adams, who had made the same move in 1838.

Adams was born in Dublin in 1793. He studied at Dublin University and at the College of Surgeons where his work was supervised by Abraham Colles. After a period of study in the leading Continental hospitals, Adams was appointed as a surgeon to the Charitable Infirmary in 1818. The medical school which he established in the stable of his home near Marlborough Street came to an untimely end when it was attacked and burnt by an irate mob objecting to the practice of body snatching. In 1826 Adams, in association with Richard Carmichael, founded the Richmond School for Medicine and Surgery which was attached to the Richmond Hospital.

In 1827 Adams published a communication in the *Dublin Hospital Reports* entitled 'Cases of Diseases of the Heart Accompanied with Pathological Observations'. In this paper Adams described a patient who suffered from blackouts associated with a slow pulse. The patient was a sixty-eight year old revenue officer whom Adams attended just as he was recovering from an episode of unconsciousness. His pulse rate was only 30 and his doctor informed Adams that:

> he had been in almost continual attendance on this gentleman for the last seven years; and that during that period he had seen him, he is quite certain, in not less than 20 apoplectic attacks. Before each of them he was observed, for a day or two, heavy and lethargic with loss of memory. He would fall down in a state of complete irreversibility and was on several occasions hurt by the fall. When they attacked him, his pulse would become even slower than usual, his breathing loudly stertorous.[5]

7.2 The Richmond Surgical Hospital, opened in 1811

This institution had many famous surgeons on its staff, among them Robert Adams and Richard Carmichael. On New Year's Day 1847 the first operation to be carried out under anaesthesia in Ireland was performed in this hospital (see chapter 11)

From Widdess' *The Richmond, Whitworth and Hardwicke Hospitals* (1972)

ROBERT ADAMS

E Sweeney

7.3 Robert Adams (1793-1875)

Adams was a surgeon who made major contributions to
medicine, especially cardiology. According to Cameron he
was a short, stout man, with a chubby face. He was very
fond of horses and he always had a good one to draw his
well-known chaise.

Adams was the first to appreciate that cerebral symptoms may be caused by disorders of the cardiac rhythm. Nearly twenty years later, William Stokes published further observations on this condition which included a careful analysis of Adams' case. The names of both men are now linked together as the condition is known as Stokes-Adams Syndrome.

Adams had a special interest in joint pathology and was the first to describe a synovial cyst. His description appeared in the *Dublin Journal of Medical Science* in 1840. It was not until 1877 that an English doctor, William Baker, reported his own observations on synovial cysts, giving rise to the common eponym Baker Cysts for popliteal cysts. In 1857 Adams published a classic book on rheumatoid arthritis entitled A *Treatise on Rheumatic Gout or Chronic Rheumatic Arthritis of all the Joints*. Eight years later, at the age of seventy-four, he travelled to France and presented his work on rheumatic diseases to the Surgical Society of Paris. The president of the society received him with great honour.

Adams became regius professor of surgery at Trinity College in 1861 when he was seventy years old. He was one of the most enthusiastic teachers and writers of the Dublin school. In an introductory lecture he told his students:

> Nor do we, the physicians and surgeons of this large hospital establishment, shrink from the responsibilities which attach to us as your clinical instructors. We shall be found at our posts, and we expect of you daily punctuality, and that you shall not when here be mere 'walkers' of the hospital wards, but attentive listeners and observers. On our parts we tell you, we can have no greater pleasure than to give instruction to an attentive class of students, and such a class, we are happy to say, we are accustomed to have in these hospitals.[6]

The teachers, of course, had other pleasures apart from lecturing to attentive classes. In 1837 they formed a social club and Dominic Corrigan became secretary. The membership of physicians and surgeons included among others William Stokes, Robert Graves, Arthur Jacob and Abraham Colles. On 6 September 1837 thirty members of the club dined at Molony's at a total cost of £8.8s.8¼d which included candles, carriages, a hamper, and alcoholic beverages costing £3.14s.9½d.

CHAPTER 8

The Pathological Society of Dublin

Despite all the developments in research and teaching, there was still no suitable scientific forum in Dublin where surgeons and physicians pursuing original work could present their cases and observations to each other. The time was now ripe for such a development and in 1838 a group of doctors met to draw up the constitution for a society which would become known as the Pathological Society of Dublin. The object of the new society was to cultivate the study of pathology and to advance the diagnosis and treatment of diseases by relating pre-mortem symptoms and signs to post-mortem findings. The great strength of the society lay in the fact that it brought surgeon, physician and obstetrician together, thus encouraging a spirit of mutual co-operation in the pursuit of knowledge.

The first joint secretaries of the Pathological Society were William Stokes and his brother in-law Robert Smith. Smith was born in Dublin in 1807 and was the son of an English father and an Irish mother. He attended the School of Physic and the College of Surgeons and was apprenticed to Richard Carmichael, one of the most able teachers of the period and the founder, with Robert Adams, of a very successful private school. In 1838, after a number of surgical posts, Smith joined his teachers on the staff of the Richmond Hospital and taught in their medical school.

According to the historian Cameron, Smith was 'one of the most distinguished anatomists and surgeons which Ireland has produced and as a teacher he has rarely been equalled'.[1] Not only was Smith an excellent teacher but he was also a superb linguist and a prolific writer. In 1847 he published his *Treatise on Fractures in the Vicinity of the Joints*, a book of 314 pages with 200 fine illustrations. The book established his reputation and was destined to become a classic of surgical literature. It contains the first description of the wrist fracture which subsequently became known as Smith's Fracture. It has also been described as the Reversed Colles Fracture since the deformity is the opposite to that sustained in a Colles Fracture. In 1847 the chairs of anatomy and surgery were separated in the School of Physic and Smith was appointed to the chair of surgery. In the same year he published another book, entitled *Treatise on the Pathology, Diagnosis and Treatment of Neuroma*. This work, which was illustrated with magnificent plates, described the pathological changes in several cases of neurofibromatosis. It anticipated the work of Von Recklinghausen of Strasburg on the same subject by thirty-three years. However Von Recklinghausen added to Smith's description by recognising that the fibromata arose from the terminal sheaths of cutaneous nerves. Eventually Smith became so involved in teaching and clinical research that he virtually abandoned his private practice. He was one of the main driving forces behind the Dublin Pathological Society.

Graves and Stokes inserted a notice in the *Dublin Journal of Medical Science*, 1 January 1839, announcing the inauguration of the new society:

> It gives us great pleasure to announce that this society has been organised and is now in full operation. We entertain no doubt that this society constituted as it is, will exercise the best influence on the School of Dublin.[2]

At the inauguration of the society, six presidents, two vice-presidents, two secretaries, a treasurer and a council of members were elected. Four surgeons, Richard Carmichael, Abraham Colles, Philip Crampton and James Cusack and two physicians, Robert Graves and Henry Marsh, were the first presidents. Robert Adams and William Montgomery were the vice-presidents. James Macartney and Dominic Corrigan were on the council. Macartney was sixty-eight at this time and it must have been gratifying for him to be asked by his former students to join the council of their new society. Hugh Carlisle, who had been one of Macartney's apprentices, was also a member of the new council. The previous year he had become proprietor of the Park Street School of Medicine. In 1849 he joined the new medical school of Queen's College Belfast as professor of anatomy and he brought the museum of the Park Street School to Belfast with him.

8.1 Robert Smith (1807-1876)
A co-founder with William Stokes of the Pathological Society of Dublin, Smith remained secretary to the society until his death in 1876. According to the British *Medical Journal (17 Aug 1867) Smith possessed 'a critical and observant appreciation of clinical facts, and above all a high canon of ethical judgement'.*

The venue of the society rotated every three months between the anatomical theatre of Trinity College, the Park Street School of Medicine and the Richmond Hospital School of Medicine. The members met at four o'clock every Saturday and pathological specimens, casts and drawings were presented. It was necessary to meet every week because they wanted the specimens to be 'exhibited in their recent state'. Despite the frequency of the meetings, they were well attended and there was no shortage of high quality communications. Many of the members were leading figures in the profession in Ireland. James Bovell, who was to become William Osler's mentor during his formative years in Canada, was also a founder member of the society. There were on average four presentations at each meeting and abridged reports of the proceedings were published in the *Dublin Journal of Medical Science*. Great stress was placed on the clinical aspect of the presentations, as is clear from the first report of the council:

> The Members were deeply convinced that without the most careful attention to symptomatology and the most faithful record of the history, diagnosis, and treatment in every case, but little advantage would be obtained by the description, however minute, of morbid structures; and it was not to be forgotten that the purely descriptive part of the science has been already extensively cultivated at home and abroad. It was in the practical application of the truths of pathology that the Society felt that there was still an hiatus to be filled up, and it wished to assist in placing the study of morbid anatomy on its true basis, and showing what it could, and what it could not effect.[3]

The proceedings of the society demonstrate the high standards of both clinical observation and pathological description achieved by members of the society. They also show the great limitations under which the physicians and surgeons worked at that time. Without antibiotics, they watched helplessly as many of their patients succumbed to overwhelming infection. Surgical therapy was also very limited before the introduction of anaesthesia and antiseptic techniques. Patients died from painful and disfiguring conditions and many of the specimens presented at the society's meetings came from post mortems on children and young adults. The therapies resorted to at the time, often in desperation, show that the physicians and surgeons were still greatly influenced by traditional practices such as bleeding, the use of leeches, emetics, purging, blistering and cupping (placing the rim of a heated glass cup on the skin to produce bruising). The moderating influence of the leaders of the school, in particular of Robert Graves, helped to reduce the over-enthusiastic use of many of these 'remedies'. From the very beginning, members of the society were aware of the potential importance of their observations. It was pointed out, for instance, that where a doubt might arise as to priority of discovery, the reference could be made to the records of the cases presented at the meetings of the society and it could be clearly established who was the first to make a particular observation.

The first clinical meeting of the society took place on 10 November 1838 with Robert Graves in the chair. The first case presented was an aneurysm of the aorta and the presenter was George Green. Aneurysms were presented frequently at subsequent meetings of the society and members of the Dublin school developed a particular expertise in their management. The second case was presented by Richard Carmichael and was entitled 'Ulcerated communication between the gall bladder and stomach':

> Mr Carmichael exhibited the liver, gall bladder and stomach of an individual who had laboured under symptoms of hepatic disease for many years. The gall bladder was thickened, much diminished in capacity, and its cavity occupied by a calculus the size of a pigeon's egg; it adhered to the stomach and communicated with it by a small opening, the result of adhesion and recent ulceration. The symptoms immediately preceding death, were great irritability of the stomach, and constant vomiting of yellow bile, which nothing could alleviate.[4]

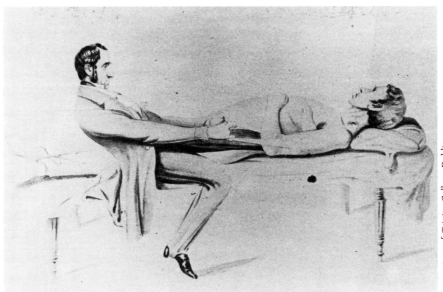

By courtesy of Trinity College Dublin

8.2 Smith treating a dislocated shoulder

Smith's appointment to the chair of surgery at Trinity College in 1849 was condemned by the College of Surgeons who saw it as an infringement of their rights and the surgeons refused to recognise the surgical lectures given in the university. As a result, despite the protestations of the surgical colleges of London and Dublin, the university introduced its own diploma in surgery in 1851.

Robert Graves exhibited an abdominal tumour which obliterated the vena cava. He described a murmur which was heard when the patient lay on his back but which ceased on assuming the erect posture. He also noted that the left epigastric mammary and intercostal veins were 'in a varicose condition'. Robert Smith presented a preparation showing a fracture of the tibia and fibula and William Stokes presented a preparation in wax demonstrating the intestinal lesions of typhoid.

In the weeks that followed several further interesting cases were presented to the society. William Stokes presented cases of intra-thoracic cancer; William Montgomery, the professor of midwifery in the School of Physic, presented a series of uterine polypi, and Robert Graves exhibited a case of chronic pleuritis. Joseph O'Ferrall presented a case of kidney disease which included the finding of albumen in the urine and a specific gravity which was always under 1006. Robert Harrison, professor of anatomy and chirurgery, described a case of ulcerated stricture of the oesophagus and how an attempt was made to support the patient before death by injecting port wine through a tube which they had pushed with difficulty past the stricture.

On 16 March 1839 Abraham Colles presented a diseased hip joint which had been taken from the body of Dr Robert Perceval who had been the main instigator behind the foundation of Sir Patrick Dun's Hospital as a teaching hospital for the School of Physic. Perceval when 'giving his last directions to his family, requested that any portion of his remains which might be made available to the cause of science should be laid before the Society'.[5] On 20 April 1839 Abraham Colles was chairman of the meeting and the first case 'Chronic endocarditis with permanent patency of the aortic valves' was presented by Dominic Corrigan.

Students were permitted to attend meetings of the Pathological Society. At the end of the session a gold medal was awarded to the student with the best essay on some aspect of pathology, chosen by the council of the society. This was regarded as the highest distinction obtainable by a student at the time. Francis Cruise, one of Corrigan's resident clinical clerks, recalled attending meetings with Corrigan: 'Late in my student days, I was fascinated by these meetings and the sound instruction they imparted. Still later, I often prepared the specimens under his direction, and listened with delight to his comments upon them.'[6] Stokes' son, also named William, who

8.3 William Stokes (1804-1878)

He was described by Sir George Paget, professor of medicine at Cambridge, as the greatest physician of his time in Europe.

70

71

became a leading Dublin surgeon wrote later in his life that he would:

> ever cherish among the pleasantest reminiscences of his student life the
> meetings of the Pathological Society, where, in common with the other
> students, he was so deeply impressed with the earnestness, zeal, and
> enthusiasm exhibited by so many distinguished members of the society, whose
> communications, as a rule, gave evidence, not only of close and accurate
> observation, but at times of that eloquence that is ever a product of a genuine
> love of truth.[7]

The society conferred honorary diplomas upon distinguished pathologists
not resident in Ireland. Doctors honoured in this way included Astley
Cooper, Benjamin Brodie, William Alison, Thomas Hodgkin, Richard Bright,
Robert Todd and Thomas Addison in Great Britain; Pierre C A Louis, Jean
Cruveilhier and Gabriel Andral in France, and Johann L Schonlein and Carl
Rokitansky in Germany and Austria. Within ten years of its foundation
similar societies were established at centres around the world including
London, Liverpool, Birmingham and Philadelphia. The council of the society
attributed this growing interest in clinical pathology to the 'successful and
persevering exertions of the Pathological Society of Dublin'.

CHAPTER 9

William Wilde:
Surgeon, Antiquary, Writer

William Wilde made significant contributions not only to medicine but also to literature and archaeology. He was an accomplished man in his own right, although he is mainly remembered today as the father of Oscar Wilde, the brilliant Irish wit and dramatist. Wilde was born in 1815, the son of a doctor with a practice in County Roscommon. He was apprenticed to Abraham Colles at Dr Steevens' Hospital in 1832. During Wilde's undergraduate days most of the students at Dr Steevens' Hospital attended the Park Street School of Medicine. James William Cusack, the resident surgeon in the hospital, also taught at the school and he had a major influence on Wilde's training.

Cusack was one of the founders of the Park Street School of Medicine and it might be argued that it was he rather than Graves who first introduced bedside teaching to Dublin. However, there was a difference of approach as Cusack was actually in the bed when he taught! His lectures usually took place in the early hours of the morning. Charles Lever, the novelist, was a fellow student with Wilde in Dr Steevens' and was well known for his sense of humour and practical jokes. On one occasion Lever was the first of the class to arrive for Cusack's morning lecture. When he arrived at the bedroom he found a notice saying that the surgeon had gone on

---

9.1   Mont Cenis by J M W Turner

In 1819 Graves travelled by coach across the Alps through the Mont Cenis pass. On the journey he was joined by Turner and together they visited Lake Como, Milan and Venice before travelling south to Rome by way of Bologna and Foligno. Art historians agree that this first Italian journey marked the most significant turning point in Turner's painting; in the following years he made his remarkable advances in portraying light as colour.

By courtesy of Birmingham Museums and Art Gallery

an urgent house call and would not be taking class that morning. Lever pocketed the notice and then, having put on Cusack's red silk nightcap, he hopped into bed and drew the blankets up about him. When the other students arrived, still half asleep, they were subjected to one of the most unusual lectures of their careers until the moment when Lever could contain himself no longer and started to laugh. For many years Wilde took great pleasure in relating this story. Cusack became professor of surgery in the School of Physic later in his career and he was also one of the six foundation presidents of the Pathological Society.

Wilde stayed in Dr Steevens' Hospital for four years before moving to the Rotunda Hospital to study midwifery. Here he wrote his first medical work, a treatise on spina bifida, and came first in the annual prize examination. However, he had been ill during the examination and collapsed shortly after it. Within a few days his condition appeared hopeless and it was thought that he had typhus. Robert Graves was asked to come and see his student for whom he prescribed a glass of strong ale to be taken every hour. The student revived and when Graves saw him next morning he was sleeping comfortably. Later when Graves was looking for a doctor to attend a patient on a health-seeking cruise to the Holy Land, he approached Wilde. He thought the trip would benefit Wilde who suffered from asthma. There was also another factor which may have been considered when the cruise was suggested to Wilde. He had just become the father of his first illegitimate child. In later years there would be at least two others.

During the journey Wilde experienced several exciting incidents which he later described in his book, *Narrative of a Voyage to Madeira, Teneriffe and Along the Shores of the Mediterranean*. When they arrived in Egypt Wilde procured two guides and three donkeys and set off across the desert to explore the tombs and pyramids of Sakara and Dashur. Having investigated the chambers of the Sakara pyramid he determined to visit the ibis mummy-pits, but when he arrived at the pits he found to his annoyance that he had forgotten to bring any source of lighting with him. Undeterred, Wilde decided to go down and explore the pits without illumination. By using foot holes cut in the wall, he and his guide climbed down a shaft to a narrow vault some thirty feet (about nine metres) below the surface. A series of chambers extended for a considerable distance on all sides of the vault. Alec, the guide, led the way:

> All was utter blackness; but Alec, who had left all his garments above, took me by the hand, and led me in a stooping posture some way amidst broken pots, sharp stones, and heaps of rubbish, that sunk under us at every step; then placing me on my face, at a particularly narrow part of the gallery,

9.2   James Cusack (1788-1861)
The night before a critical operation Cusack would lie awake for hours thinking of the best way to approach it and he was scrupulous in his post-operative care. He was a hospitable man and his houses at 7 Merrion Square and Abbeville, Kinsealy, were always open to his former apprentices.

he assumed a similar snake-like posture himself, and by a vermicular motion, and keeping hold of his legs, I contrived to scramble through a burrow of sand and sharp bits of pottery, frequently scraping my back against the roof.... At length we arrived at a place where we could stand upright, and creeping over a vast pile of pots, and sinking in the dust of thousands of animals, we came to where we felt the urns still undisturbed, and piled up in rows.... Thousands upon thousands of the urns have been removed and broken, either in the cave or outside, where they form an immense heap, yet thousands still remain.[1]

Returning to the surface Wilde continued his journey to the pyramids of Giza where he risked his life in climbing to the top of the Great Pyramid:

I was totally unaware of the difficulty and danger of this ascent, and of its having been undertaken by but five or six travellers of late years; the natives themselves never scaling it but for some reward.[2]

Wilde was assisted by two guides during the ascent:

Some idea may be formed of my feelings, when it is recollected, that all these stones of such a span are highly polished, are set at an angle less than 45 degrees, and that the places we had to grip with our hands and feet, were often not two inches wide, and their height above the ground upwards of four hundred feet! A single slip of the foot, or a slight gust of wind, and from our position, we must all three have been dashed to atoms, long before reaching the ground. On gaining the top my guides gave vent to sundry demonstrations of satisfaction, clapping me on the back, patting my head, kissing my hands.... From all this I began to suspect something wonderful had been achieved.[2]

Wilde became fascinated by archaeological research, an interest he maintained throughout his life. He made significant contributions to Irish archaeology and was the first antiquary to stress the importance of lake dwellings. He also became very interested in 'trachoma', an infectious eye disease which was a very common cause of blindness in the Orient. This interest awakened in him a desire to study diseases of the eye. During his voyage Wilde had made several original observations on various aspects of natural history and when he returned to Dublin Macartney encouraged him to present his findings at a meeting of the British Association in Birmingham in 1839.

9.3 Trinity College Dublin, by Tom Nisbett
Trinity College, the oldest university in Ireland, was founded in 1592 by Queen Elizabeth I on the site of an ancient monastery, All Hallows, which had been dispossessed more than fifty years earlier by Henry VIII.

It must have been a source of some satisfaction to Macartney to witness the success of pupils such as Graves, Corrigan and Wilde. His own career in the School of Physic had continued to be punctuated by a series of disputes with the authorities of the college, one of which took place in 1835 and finally led to his resignation. This dispute arose when the King's professor of the practice of medicine, Charles Lendrick, asked the board to stop Macartney lecturing at the same time as himself because all the students were going to the anatomy lectures. Macartney refused to comply as he had been lecturing at that particular time, between three and four in the afternoon, before Lendrick was appointed. The board was infuriated by this response and so it was ordered that 'the Anatomy House be closed every day during the hour from three to four, and that a copy of this order shall be posted on the College gate and on the hall door of the Anatomy House'.[3] The next day, at three o'clock, the college registrar, together with a college porter and a locksmith, placed a padlock and a placard on the outer door of the Anatomy House. This action led to a further deterioration in relationships and after a number of other exchanges Macartney resigned his office in 1837. A year later his book entitled A *Treatise on Inflammation* was published by Longmans. The work received very enthusiastic reviews in the leading medical journals of the period. In the following years he continued to write and to travel in England and on

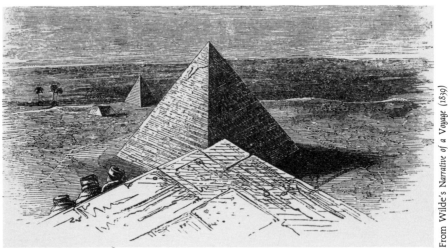

From Wilde's Narrative of a Voyage (1839)

9.4 Wilde's sketch of the view from the top of the Great Pyramid

Wilde performed the most daring feat of his life in a nightmare climb of the Great Pyramid. From a platform not more than six feet square, where it was too dangerous to stand, he looked down on a scene of intoxicating grandeur.

By courtesy of the National Library of Ireland

9.5   William Wilde (1815-1876)

He was one of the most brilliant and diversified members of the Irish school of medicine.

the Continent. On Monday morning, 9 March 1843, Macartney went into his study to make the final adjustments to a paper he was preparing, 'The development of faculties in the animal', to be read before the College of Physicians. He wrote:

> The last great event is the extinction of the systemic functions which is commonly called death. As soon as the vitality of the tissue is lost, the body becomes subject to the laws of inorganic matter. The greater part of it is exhaled and is carried by the winds and clouds to distant regions, and finally they descend with rains to fertilise the earth. We thus repay our great debt to nature, and return the elements of our bodies to the common storehouse. Thus ends this strange, eventful history.

> All forms that perish, other forms supply:
> (By turns we catch the vital breath and die,)
> Like bubbles on the sea of matter borne
> They rise, they break, and to that sea return.[4]

These were the last words from Macartney's hand, as he died at his desk shortly after writing them.

After Wilde had presented his research to the British Association in Birmingham, he went to London to begin his study of ophthalmology. While working in the English capital Wilde formed a lasting friendship with Robert Todd, another of Graves' former pupils. Wilde also became a friend of

9.6 Allgemeines Krankenhaus

Vienna set a model for the rest of Europe with its hospital devoted not only to teaching and research but also to the care of the poor.

By courtesy of the Institute of Medical History, Vienna

Sir James Clarke, the court physician, who introduced him to London society where he soon made a name for himself as his son would do later in the century.

After several months in London, Wilde decided to visit some of the famous Continental clinics, starting with Vienna. Towards the end of the eighteenth century, the emperor of Austria, Joseph II, son of Maria Theresa, had amalgamated most of the smaller hospitals of Vienna and created the Allgemeines Krankenhaus, the famous general hospital. This hospital contained over a hundred wards and more than a thousand patients. It was divided into three main parts: the medical and surgical hospital, the maternity hospital and the psychiatric section. The hospital was built in the form of a vast quadrangle enclosing about a dozen small squares.

Wilde was surprised to find that bedside teaching in the hospital was still carried out through the medium of Latin. This practice had declined earlier in the century in Dublin as the new teachers had insisted on using the vernacular. He was also surprised to find that the beds were not curtained off as at home, and that the nurses slept on the wards. When the consultant entered the wards the patients and nurses were expected to kiss his hand, a custom that cannot have helped with the problem of cross-infection. Wilde thought it a servile practice and he was pleased to note that some of the younger consultants were happy to accept what might be called a token gesture if their staff simply muttered 'Küss' die hand'!

Bedside teaching was the accepted way of clinical teaching. However, students were not encouraged to walk the wards unsupervised. The teaching ward rounds were very large with over one hundred students in a ward at times. Wilde was particularly interested in the work of Professor Josef Skoda who taught diseases of the chest at a private clinic. Skoda made great use of the stethoscope and of course Wilde would have been familiar with the pioneering work of Stokes in Dublin. Although Wilde thought Skoda was a superb diagnostician he did not rate him as highly at treatment as Graves or Stokes.

Another doctor who greatly impressed Wilde was the Czech, Carl Rokitansky, whom he predicted would soon have an international reputation. Rokitansky devoted all his time to the study of pathology and the interesting cases in the hospital all came to autopsy. Rokitansky, Skoda and Semmelweis were the pioneers of the new Viennese School of Medicine. During his stay in Vienna Wilde became very friendly with Semmelweis, the great reformer of obstetric practice, and afterwards he corresponded with him for many years. Every morning at eight o'clock,

Rokitansky went with his assistants and students to the mortuary of the hospital. Four to six bodies were usually examined by Rokitansky over a two-hour period, during which he called out his findings to an assistant who sat at a desk taking notes. Students studying under Rokitansky were required to perform an autopsy each day and to report on the findings to the professor. Towards the end of their course Rokitansky introduced teaching on the use of the microscope.

Wilde observed that Rokitansky, like most reformers, encountered some stiff opposition:

> Different from all other pathologists, Rokitansky does not engage in the study or treatment of disease during life — he is not a practical physician, and seldom sees one of the many hundreds of cases whose bodies he dissects. This has been loudly exclaimed against by many, who say that here morbid anatomy has completely usurped the place of pathology; but though it presents an anomaly peculiar to this school, it undoubtedly possesses many advantages.[5]

When Wilde left Vienna he travelled at a leisurely pace through Germany, spending some time at Dresden and Heidelberg and studying surgery under Dieffenbach, a pioneer of surgery in Berlin.

On returning to Dublin Wilde set up practice as an eye and ear specialist at 15 Westland Row and established his own Eye and Ear Hospital. Graves joined him as a consulting physician. For a long time Wilde's hospital was the only one in Ireland and Great Britain in which aural surgery was taught. As a consequence, many students, undergraduates and postgraduates came to it from abroad, particularly from America.

Wilde's hospital was very successful and he changed its location to larger premises as it expanded. In 1848 the medical school building in Park Street, where Wilde had attended lectures as a student, came on the market. When it was being built the surgeon James Cusack, one of the proprietors, had insisted that it should be constructed like a Methodist chapel so that it could be sold quickly should the school fail. As a result the building was large and roomy and ideal for Wilde's purpose; he adapted it to accommodate twenty public patients and there were also three private rooms, an operating theatre, an out-patients department, living quarters for a house surgeon and a lecture room.

Wilde became one of the greatest aurists of his time and he helped to place the subject of ear diseases on a scientific footing. He invented many instruments including the first dressing forceps and an aural snare known as Wilde's Snare. One of the operative approaches he devised for mastoiditis is still known as Wilde's Incision. His name is also associated with Wilde's

9.7 Carl Rokitansky (1804-1878)

*One of the greatest pathologists the world has known,
Rokitansky was pre-eminent as a teacher in Vienna.*

85

cone of light, an optical appearance on the external aspect of the membrana tympani. This is known on the Continent as Politzer's cone of light. Politzer was a professor of otology in Vienna and he described the phenomenon later in the century. Wilde also established the role of the middle ear in the genesis of aural infections. In 1853 Wilde's textbook *Practical Observations on Aural Surgery and the Nature and Treatment of Diseases of the Ear* was published; now a classic, it has been described as the first textbook of importance on the subject. Wilde's book is based largely on bedside observations and investigations:

> I have laboured, and I trust not in vain, to expose error and establish truth; to lay down just principles for an accurate diagnosis of Diseases of the Ear; to rescue their treatment from empiricism, and found it upon the well-established laws of modern pathology, practical surgery, and reasonable therapeutics.[6]

An American edition of Wilde's book was brought out by Addinel Hewson, who had been a pupil of Wilde's in Dublin. It was also translated into German and remained a standard textbook in the English-speaking world and in Germany and Austria for many years. Wilde was recruited by the government to act as a medical census commissioner and he did remarkable work on the analysis of health information in the census returns of 1841 and 1851. The population of Dublin in 1841 was 232,000 and the majority of the people in the city were paupers living on the borderline of necessity. His report on the 1851 census has become a standard work of reference on the Great Famine which devastated Ireland during the years 1845-1849. Wilde also wrote a book describing his experiences on the Continent, entitled *Austria. Its Literary, Scientific and Medical Institutions*, which was published in 1843. The previous year he had become editor of the *Dublin Quarterly Journal of Medical Science* (formerly the *Dublin Journal of Medical Science*).

Wilde was aware of the importance of the journal when he took over its editorship. After reviewing all the medical periodicals which had been published in Ireland he wrote of the *Dublin Quarterly Journal of Medical Science*:

> It has now reached to twenty-eight goodly volumes, in which will be found the best record of the modern school of medicine in Dublin; for, without distinction of persons, we may safely say, that there is no medical man of eminence in this city, or indeed in Ireland, who has not contributed to its pages; and the volumes already published embody one of the largest collections of original facts and communications in medicine, pathology, surgery and midwifery that can in all probability be found in any journal in Europe.[7]

When Wilde returned to Dublin Jacob was the leading eye surgeon in the city. He was twenty-five years older than Wilde and was well established at the time as professor of anatomy and physiology at the Royal College of Surgeons. For many years Jacob had championed various aspects of medical reform in his periodical, the *Dublin Medical Press*. He never hesitated to criticise colleagues and his sarcasm could be biting. Yet he appeared to lack the ability to control a class of unruly students. One of his students, Alexander Macalister, who later filled the chair of anatomy in the School of Physic and subsequently in Cambridge, recalled one of Jacob's classes:

> My respected teacher in physiology, Dr Jacob, although a man of immense erudition and extremely kind to his students, had not the knack of keeping a class in order. I was present on one occasion, I think in 1859, when a student incautiously directed his pea-shooter so that the pellet struck Dr Jacob on his spectacles. This insult was too much for the irascible old gentleman who stopped, turned towards the culprit and addressed him. 'I see you, and you are a coward, to insult an old man, but old as I am I'll fight you'. Then pulling off his coat and squaring his fists he said 'Come on now, you coward'. Needless to relate, the student did not respond, and the class broke up.[8]

Jacob was an introvert who led an abstemious life, whereas Wilde was an extrovert who enjoyed the limelight. Wilde's appointment as editor of the *Dublin Quarterly Journal of Medical Science* may have annoyed Jacob as he had lost the post of assistant editor in 1836 through the intemperate nature of his contributions. In any case, Jacob showed little restraint when he wrote about Wilde in his weekly journal, the *Dublin Medical Press*. He claimed that Wilde was using his position as a census commissioner to inflate his own importance and to attract private patients. In his articles Jacob misspelt Wilde's name deliberately to annoy him, referring to him as Wild. On another occasion, when discussing the itinerary of an American doctor who was visiting European clinics, Jacob wrote sarcastically: 'In Dublin he is sure to dine with Dr Stokes and sup with Surgeon Wilde.' Wilde showed more restraint in writing about Jacob. After reviewing the history of Irish medical periodicals in the *Dublin Quarterly Journal of Medical Science*, Wilde mentioned the establishment of the *Dublin Medical Press* and he concluded with the observation:

> Were we writing as Historian simply, and not in our Editorial capacity, we might offer some remarks on the tone and style of the *Dublin Medical Press* but, under existing circumstances we deem it more proper to refrain.[7]

Wilde married in 1851 and around this time he also moved residence from 15 to 21 Westland Row. It was here that his two sons, Willie and Oscar, were born. The houses at Westland Row overlooked the grounds of Trinity College, making it convenient for Wilde to attend the meetings of the Pathological Society when they were held in the anatomy theatre on Saturday afternoons.

CHAPTER 10

The Great Famine

The Irish school of medicine developed in the decade of the greatest national distress that Ireland has ever experienced. Between 1841 and 1851 the population of the country dropped by over two million as a result of the Great Famine. However, even during the earlier years of the century, poverty, malnutrition, poor sanitation and virulent epidemic diseases were causing devastation. Robert Graves estimated that one third of all those born in this period died before their first birthday, one half before their eight birthday and two thirds before their thirty-eighth year.

Despite the prevalence of serious disease among the poor, there were virtually no medical services for this section of the population in many parts of the country, and although members of the Irish school of medicine made strenuous efforts to remedy this situation, they made little progress. In 1838 the Poor Relief (Ireland) Act came into law and the country was divided into unions, each of which had to construct a workhouse for the relief of the destitute. Relief could only be obtained in the workhouse and preference was given to the aged and infirm. Able-bodied paupers had to work within the workhouse, hence its name. This system, which was based on a similar system in England, was totally unsuitable and inadequate to cope with the problems of poverty at this time. The doctors who strove to care for the sick poor did so at tremendous risk to themselves. Facilities were virtually non-existent and epidemics were rampant. In 1840 an epidemic of typhus swept through the country and many doctors died. In 1842 the British House of Commons began preparing a Bill which would be known as the Medical Charities Act. This Bill, which was passed the following year, dealt with the provision of support for dispensaries and fever hospitals, the remuneration of medical officers and the administration of the system. William Stokes and James Cusack went to London to give evidence before the committee drafting the Bill. They stressed the inadequacies of the medical services, particularly in rural areas, and the tremendous pressures on the country doctors:

> The Irish physician is often exposed to contagion in its most concentrated force when himself under the influence of cold, wet, fatigue, and hunger, as he labours among the poor, passing from hovel to hovel in wild, thinly populated but extensive districts. He has often to ride for many hours in the worst weather, and at night, enduring great fatigue, while himself a prey to mental as to physical suffering, for if we add to such labour the injurious influence which the knowledge of danger must have on the system of a man feeling that he is struck down by the disease under which he has seen so many sink, and tortured by the thought of leaving a young family unprovided for .... [1]

They produced figures which showed that the mortality of army officers in combat was only half that of Irish medical practitioners and that 25 per cent of Irish doctors died in discharge of their duties. 'Such a number of my pupils' said Stokes, 'have been cut off by typhus fever as to make me feel very uneasy when any of them take a dispensary office in Ireland. I look upon it almost as going into battle.'[1] Stokes and Cusack asked for adequate remuneration for doctors who attended dispensaries and fever hospitals, and appropriate support for the widows and children of doctors who died in the course of their duties.

Stokes, Cusack, Graves and Wilde were members of a small voluntary group called the Medical Temporary Relief Committee, which was established at the suggestion of the Church of Ireland Archbishop of Dublin. They distributed money to the families of medical men who were experiencing hardship. This relief must have been welcome, but it cannot have gone very far to alleviate the distress. Another voluntary body, the Medical Benevolent Fund, was established by Richard Carmichael in 1842 to help in similar situations. This body still functions today, providing assistance to the families of doctors in financial difficulties. Despite the appeals of the physicians and surgeons on behalf of the sick poor, no immediate official action was taken. Eventually in 1851 the Medical Charities Act was introduced and this established a dispensary service throughout Ireland for poor people.

Meanwhile the country experienced the most appalling ravages of the Great Famine. The potato had for many years been the staple diet of the Irish people. In 1846 and again in 1847 and 1848 the crop failed because

10.1 A Victorian Irish doctor on house calls

Many dispensary doctors died each year from infectious diseases. Most were men in the prime of life and the most common infection was typhus, a disease conveyed by lice, which was permanently present amongst the poor at that time.

From T Stuart's *Programme of Proceedings of the Annual Meeting of the BMA in Dublin* (1887)

of a fungal infection (phytophthora infestans). People began to starve and in their malnourished state they succumbed in their thousands to typhus, dysentery, relapsing fever and scurvy. Stokes has recorded that during the famine many cases of starvation were admitted into the wards of the Meath Hospital:

> They had all a dreadful similarity ... weak, cold and shrivelled, they lay uncomplaining, more like cadavers than living human beings. They seldom asked for food or even drink. The pulse was quick and feeble; the skin earthy and of the colour of parchment; and the tongue pale.[2]

The government allowed market forces free reign during the famine, and great quantities of meat and corn left the country as landlords sold them abroad. Physicians watched in horror as the people starved and they agonised as to whether they should become involved in the political arena. Graves told his students:

> To explain the origins of that poverty which excites the sympathy even of strangers — to account for a scarcity of provisions in a country whose ports are crowded with shipping employed in carrying away corn and cattle — to investigate the sources of that pollution which has demoralized a people naturally open, frank and generous, and has rendered intemperance and improvidence the most venial parts of the national character — belongs not to statistical medicine: the duty of the physician extends not to these subjects; his employment is to alleviate the effects without discussing the causes of misery and vices; but he owes it to society — he owes it to his country — to proclaim aloud the existence of the evil.[3]

It has been estimated that over two million people fled the country, many of them going to America. Graves highlighted the terrible mortality on the crowded emigrant ships: 'There was scarcely a single ship in which typhus fever did not break out on the passage; and the mortality, as we might expect, was still greater than on land.'[4] He went on to give details of individual ships, such as the *Ceylon* with 257 steerage passengers, of whom 30 died on the voyage and 115 had fever on their arrival in North America, and the *Loosthank* with 349 steerage passengers, of whom 117 died and only 20 escaped typhus.

Many of the emigrants who survived the journey died of typhus on the streets of New York when they arrived in America. Hospital buildings were erected on Ward's Island to cope with the situation and Dr Thomas Addis Emmet, grandnephew of the Irish patriot Robert Emmet, was appointed as the first resident physician. His descriptions of the misery which he encountered make harrowing reading:

In the beginning there was no limit to the number of passengers received to satisfy the greed of the ship owner, so long as deck room could be found; and all were expected to supply their provisions. All, as a rule, were in the prime of life but there were very few whose vitality had not been already impaired by the famine before sailing ... in a few weeks, if typhus fever had not been contracted before sailing, the supply of food would become exhausted .... Through the penurious practice of the owners they (the ships) were never properly equipped and always short handed, and relied upon such aid as the male passengers might give. Consequently these vessels were frequently from 150 to 160 days making the voyage, and often after sighting land they would be driven back by adverse winds across the Atlantic again .... The mortality, therefore, was great, and the writer can recall hearing of several instances where one half of the passengers had died and been thrown overboard before the voyage was concluded.'[5]

Many doctors also died during the famine. One out of every thirteen doctors appointed to attend fever patients died on duty. One of the doctors to die in this way was Valentine Flood. He lectured for a time in the Windmill Street School of Anatomy in London before returning to Dublin to work in the poorer areas of the city. He was the first to describe the superior glenohumeral ligament of the shoulder joint and he also wrote a number of books of which his *Surgical Anatomy of the Arteries* was the most highly acclaimed. He was appointed by the Board of Health to the fever hospital at Tubrid, County Tipperary, in 1847, where he was fatally infected with typhus.

In an editorial in September 1847, the *Dublin Medical Press* protested against the 'pest houses' in which doctors were expected to work. There were between three and four hundred of them in the country at that time. The same issue reported the death of a young doctor named George Vickers Dunne, a relative of the editor Arthur Jacob: 'The mud walls of an old cottage, eked out with boarding and covered with straw, formed his "fever hospital" in which nearly sixty patients were under treatment at the time he contracted the disease (typhus), of which he died after a few days illness.'[6]

The stress of the famine years brought about an unfortunate rift between Robert Graves and Dominic Corrigan. Corrigan had written a pamphlet in 1846 predicting the likelihood of famine if the potato crop failed. When his predictions were realised within a very short period, the government established the Central Board of Health with powers to open fever hospitals and to provide medical assistance. Dominic Corrigan, Philip Crampton and Robert Kane were the three doctors appointed to the board by the government. The College of Physicians was annoyed because it had not

From *Illustrated London News* (10 May 1851)

10.2 Departure of the 'Nimrod' and 'Athlone' steamers from Cork with emigrants for Liverpool

In the first half of 1847 over 100,000 Irish paupers were said to have arrived in Liverpool. Typhus ravaged the impoverished emigrants and the registrar-general wrote: 'In itself, one of the unhealthiest towns of the kingdom, Liverpool, has for a year been the hospital and cemetery of Ireland'. (Quoted by Graves in his Clinical Lectures, p 73.)

From T A Emmet's *Incidents of My Life* (1911), Putmans, New York

10.3 The State Emigrant Refuge and Hospital Institutions, Ward's Island, New York

The emigrants were usually in a helpless condition on arrival in port. On opening the hatches the health officer was frequently compelled to have the fire-engine pump started so that the deadly atmosphere below might be purified before the passengers could be removed.

been asked for nominations.

The Central Board of Health could not cope with the extent of the devastation and it soon came under attack. The medical officers attending fever cases were paid five shillings per day in addition to any permanent salary. The medical profession was outraged by this meagre amount of money as many of these doctors were dying from typhus. Graves mounted a bitter attack of thirty pages on the Board of Health and he singled out his colleagues for special condemnation. His letter was published in the *Dublin Journal of Medical Science* and Graves addressed it to William Wilde, the editor of the journal:

> Having been my pupil, and diligently attended my clinical instruction, you may, perhaps, bear not an unwilling testimony to the fact, that I ever used my best efforts to stimulate my pupils to exertion, and devoted all my energies to awaken in them a proper estimate of the responsibility they were to incur when they entered upon the practice of their profession. Having laboured for upwards of twenty years in instructing a numerous class of students, I may assert with truth, that there are few classes or dispensaries which are not occupied by some of my pupils. And consequently, at this present calamitous period, I am destined to feel a mixed sensation of pleasure and of sorrow; — of pleasure at finding that my labours have not been altogether unavailing, as is testified by the zeal and ability of many who have formed part of my clinical class; — of sorrow, caused by receiving almost daily accounts that some have sickened and others have actually fallen victims to the present epidemic.[7]

Graves went on to write about one of his former pupils, Oliver Curran, who was appointed by the Board of Health to treat fever cases. He refused to accept their payment of five shillings a day as it was considered such a derisory sum. He resigned the post and instead he worked voluntarily with the patients. Wilde described Curran as the impersonation of charity. He paid the ultimate price for his generosity and Graves had to add a sad footnote to his letter, just before publication, announcing Curran's death from typhus fever. His death, as Graves pointed out, caused national indignation.

Graves included in his letter a bitter personal attack on his friends and colleagues, Kane, Corrigan and Crampton. Kane was at this time a well known and reputable professor of chemistry. Graves observed that his 'friend Sir Robert Kane has succeeded in the process of self-analysis so as to eliminate and get rid of the MD element from himself, as being the most unprofitable portion of his composition'.[7] Graves was equally hard on Corrigan and accused him of having delusions of grandeur in associating with Sir Philip

Crampton, one of the wealthiest surgeons of the period: 'But, Dr Corrigan may be excused from becoming a little giddy when he ventures into the same car with Sir Philip and, to the amazement of all, suddenly finds himself at an altitude so elevated, that his companion, although a veteran aeronaut, betrays distinct evidence of alarm.'[7] He reserved his most bitter criticism for Sir Philip Crampton. He accused him of betraying the interests of the students to whom he had lectured at the Meath Hospital.

In 1848 the debilitated population was threatened by an epidemic of cholera. Graves had made a careful study of the disease and he was the first to show clearly that cholera travelled only along lines of human communication. However, there were many, including the College of Physicians in London and the Central Board of Health in Dublin, who still held that cholera was not contagious. Cholera had advanced slowly across Europe and in 1848 it arrived in England. The Board of Health in Dublin published a circular giving the following advice:

> The Commissioners of Health are anxious to impress upon all persons the important difference that exists between cholera and fever, with respect to the mode of propagation of these epidemic diseases. Fever, it is well known, is highly contagious, or easily propagated from one individual to another; while all experience shows that cholera is rarely, if ever, contagious; consequently, the separation of the sick from the healthy, — a measure so essential in checking the spread of fever, — is not required in cholera; and the friends and relatives of persons attacked with cholera may be under no apprehension of catching the disease.[8]

The Royal College of Physicians in London gave the same advice. The Board of Health said that it was not necessary to provide special hospital accommodation and that victims of the disease should be treated at home if possible. Graves responded indignantly, claiming that the disease was contagious, and he asked:

> How can the poor of Dublin be treated for cholera at their own homes? Any man who knows the social conditions of Dublin, and the economy of the Dublin lodging-houses which the poor and struggling almost exclusively occupy, will not hesitate to pronounce it impossible. Several families not infrequently occupy one room; several individuals one bed. Even where a family has the exclusive use of a room, there is no 'spare bed' for a patient; and if the bed be given up to the sick, all the other members of the family must sit shivering and sleeping in the cold. Judicious precaution against disease! Then where are the appliances for promoting warmth, so essential in the treatment of cholera? Blankets, — there is but one for the whole family! Hot brick, jars of hot water, — there is no fire even to warm a drink;

From E Somerville and M Ross's *An Incorruptible Irishman* (1932), Nicholson and Watson, London

10.4   Sir Philip Crampton (1777-1858)

A surgeon with a large practice Crampton was said to be the most handsome and well-dressed man of his time. His sister Nancy was the great grandmother of the Irish writers Edith Somerville and Martin Ross, and of the distinguished medical scholar Sir Bertram Windle (see chapter 18). When advanced in years Crampton was heard to boast one day that he had swam across Lough Bray, ridden into Dublin, and amputated a limb before breakfast.

not even a rushlight to give the colour of warmth to the room! Yet it is here, and under such circumstances, our non-contagionist humanitarians would have the poor of Dublin treated for cholera; prepared for death would be, perhaps, the more proper phrase.[8]

Cholera spread to Ireland in 1849 and there were many deaths in Dublin and the surrounding villages. The village of Castleknock, about three miles (five kilometres) outside Dublin, lost half its inhabitants. Bray in County Wicklow also lost many of its townspeople. Graves received a letter from a relation and former pupil, Dr Graves of Rush, describing the effects of cholera on the overcrowded and malnourished population of his area:

> The disease now began to extend rapidly westward, appearing in several localities almost at the same time, seldom leaving a house without attacking several of the inhabitants, and, in some instances, sweeping off whole families .... In fact so evident had the signs of contagion now become, even to non-medical minds, that friends and relatives fled from their plague-stricken houses, leaving the sick and dying to the mercy of any one who might have sufficient courage and charity to administer to them in their hour of need.[9]

An isolation hospital was opened locally and it was only then that the progress of the epidemic slackened in Rush.

In 1849 Queen Victoria decided to visit her subjects in Ireland. Graves expressed the fear that the cholera would spread much more widely following the visit:

> These fears were much heightened, when I beheld the crowds of persons, of all classes, who sallied forth — too many of them from abodes of misery — to view the magnificent and brilliant appearance of the city on the evening of its illumination, and who thronged every place or thoroughfare, both in the city, Kingstown, and elsewhere, in which Her Majesty was expected to appear. Relatives of persons sick of cholera, those convalescent, from premonitory diarrhoea, cholera porters, nurse-tenders, and others connected with the hospitals, unable to restrain their curiosity, were everywhere mixed up and brought into close contact with those who had been previously healthy.[9]

Kingstown, now known as Dun Laoghaire, had already had cholera victims before the queen arrived. Graves' apprehensions were soon confirmed as within a week of the queen's embarkation the disease spread to many parts of the country which were previously unaffected by the epidemic. Some had feared that the epidemic was going to be worse than it actually was, but William Wilde attributed its mitigation to the fact that many areas did provide isolation facilities despite the initial official advice, and he also gave credit to the level of medical relief provided by the Central Board of Health.

Graves was obviously under great pressure when he wrote the letter which attacked Corrigan, Crampton and Kane on a personal level. Stokes once wrote that as Graves' mind was 'open and unsuspicious he occasionally fell into the error of thinking aloud without considering the nature of his audience, and of letting his wit play more freely, and his sarcasm when defending the right cut more deeply than caution might dictate'.[10] It is unfortunate that the dispute occurred, as Graves had written a letter to Corrigan in 1837 in which he praised his accomplishments:

> I have no hesitation in asserting that your papers have been of the highest order, and that they are quoted with approbation both in America and throughout Europe as containing some important discoveries in Medicine.[11]

Corrigan had worked extremely hard during the famine, trying to fulfil his duties to the best of his ability under difficult circumstances. 'After a hard day's work of hospital and private practice, it was usual for him to devote six or eight hours in tedious office work, receiving and answering from all parts of Ireland.'[12] Corrigan chose the period to apply for an honorary fellowship of the College of Physicians but he was unsuccessful. *The Lancet* had campaigned against him saying that to appoint him would be conferring approval on the deeds of the Board of Health.

The famine period was also a very difficult time for William Stokes and the misery which he witnessed affected him greatly. He too had to endure the deaths of close friends and colleagues, such as the patriot Thomas Davis and the physicians Oliver Curran and George Greene. Stokes had attended Davis when he died at the age of thirty-one from scarlet fever. Oliver Curran had been one of his favourite pupils and Stokes cared for him when he was dying from typhus. He also attended George Greene who had been appointed King's professor of medicine in the School of Physic in 1841 when Stokes himself and Corrigan were also candidates. Greene was on the council of the Dublin Pathological Society and Stokes would have known him very well. He had originally intended to become a surgeon but his hopes were dashed in 1828 when he lost his right hand at the wrist as the result of an accidental gun-shot wound. He changed his career to medicine and his extraordinary courage is exemplified by the fact that within two years he was elected a fellow of the College of Physicians. It was Greene who read the first communication to the Pathological Society of Dublin, and his final public act, performed the day before the onset of his last illness, was to attend the weekly meeting of the society. He died from typhus and at the time of his death he was gathering material for a book on the disease. All these deaths upset Stokes greatly and for a long time he agonised over whether he made the right decisions in his treatment. He strove to reassure himself:

> In many such instances the feeling is a mistaken one, for we fret for not having done that of which we had no knowledge we ought to have done, and if we do our best, why should we be dissatisfied? But still the feeling is irresistible, and comes over one like a winter cloud.[13]

CHAPTER 11

Inventions and Innovations

During the famine years in Ireland, a momentous event took place in Boston which was to revolutionise the practice of surgery. This was the first successful public demonstration of anaesthesia, on 16 October 1846, at the Massachusetts General Hospital. News of the great event crossed the Atlantic and Robert Liston carried out the first painless amputation under ether in Europe on 21 December. Eleven days later, on New Year's Day 1847, John McDonnell performed the first operation under anaesthesia in Ireland at the Richmond Hospital.

John Forbes, the editor of the *British and Foreign Medical Review*, had watched the Liston operation in London. He rushed back to his office just in time to insert a note into the next issue under the heading 'A new means of rendering surgical operations painless'. McDonnell read this note in Dublin on 30 December after his attention had been directed to it by a surgical colleague in the hospital. McDonnell had decided that same day to amputate the arm of a young girl. These amputations were traumatic events, not only for the unfortunate patient but also for the surgeon. McDonnell decided to postpone the operation for twenty-four hours while he made up an apparatus for inhaling ether vapour. He first tried it on himself, gradually losing consciousness and then recovering without ill effect. The following morning he brought the apparatus to the operating theatre where he was to be assisted by his colleagues Carmichael, Adams, Hamilton and Hutton. All these men, members of the Pathological Society of Dublin, were keenly aware of the significance of their endeavour. News of the undertaking had spread and there were many observers, including eminent surgeons and physicians and a class of students.

The first attempt to anaesthetise the girl failed, but the second was successful. Only twice during the procedure did she show any signs of discomfort and throughout her pulse rate and pupils were carefully observed. That evening McDonnell wrote a detailed account of the procedure to the editors of the *Dublin Medical Press*:

> I regard this discovery as one of the most important of this century. It will rank with vaccination, and other of the greatest benefits that medical science has bestowed on man. It adds to the long list of those benefits, and establishes another claim, in favour of that science, upon the respect and gratitude of mankind.[1]

McDonnell was born in Belfast in 1796 and educated at Trinity College and the Royal College of Surgeons. He was apprenticed to Richard Carmichael who was to assist him in his historic operation on New Year's Day 1847. He studied in Edinburgh and graduated in 1825 with Stokes, Corrigan and Ferguson.

Accounts of operations in the pre-anaesthetic era serve to emphasise the importance of the discovery of anaesthesia. A student described an operation which he witnessed in the Richmond Hospital in 1825 when Richard Carmichael removed a portion of the lower jaw of a boy. The room:

> was nearly filled with Pupils and Surgeons; the former seated on benches, the latter standing on what may be termed the stage, and obstructing and mobishly closing up its whole area. The patient ... a boy about fourteen ... was placed on the lap of an able assistant but on the first incision the boy screamed and struggled with so much violence, that it required much more than the strength applied as it was, of the many broad shouldered gentlemen surrounding him to keep him in his seat, but as to securing his head the more hands that attempted it, the worse they succeeded. A regular confusion now ensued; the operator supplicated for light, air and room; his privileged brethren thronged but the more intensely about him; .... The patient was shifted to a table, but still remained invisible: his continued screams however, and the repeated remonstrances of Mr Carmichael insisting for elbow room, assured us that the operation was still going on.[2]

After about half an hour a portion of the jaw was removed, and the specimen was passed around the students. They also saw the boy walk stoutly out of the operating room, despite his suffering and loss of blood, without deigning to avail himself of the assistance which was proffered to him on all sides.

It was around this time also that the whole practice of pathology began to change with the increased emphasis on microscopic findings. The microscope was introduced to Dublin medicine by John Houston, whose

By courtesy of RCSI

11.1 John McDonnell (1796-1892)

He concluded his account of the first operation performed under anaesthesia in Ireland with the sentence: 'It offers, in my opinion, an occasion beyond measure more worthy, for Te Deums in Christian Cathedrals, and for thanksgiving to the Author and Giver of all good, than all the victories that fire and sword have ever achieved.'

name is perpetuated in anatomy because of the rectal 'valves' or folds which have been called after him. Houston studied in the Royal College of Surgeons and graduated in medicine at Edinburgh University in 1826. He was appointed a surgeon to the City of Dublin Hospital (Baggot Street) when it opened in 1832.

Although the foundations of microscopy had been laid in the seventeenth century by men like Anton van Leeuwenhoeck of Delft and Marcello Malpighi of Bologna, microscopy did not begin to make a major impact on scientific and medical thought until the early nineteenth century. Around 1820 botanists began a systematic study of the microanatomy of plants and Robert Brown, an army surgeon, discovered the cell nucleus. A decade later Johannes Purkinje of Prague and Johannes Muller of Berlin became enthusiastic microscopists. Muller trained several talented pupils including Theodor Schwann, Friedrich Henle, Rudolf Virchow, Rudolf von Kolliker and Hermann von Helmholtz. In 1839 Schwann, a Prussian physiologist, enunciated the cell theory. In Dublin, Houston was particularly interested in Muller's work on cancer cells. In 1844 he published a paper in the *Dublin Medical Press* entitled 'The microscopic pathology of cancer'. In this paper he stated: 'I have taken every opportunity of making myself acquainted with microscopic characters of morbid growths.'[3] He described the microscopic observations he had made on tumours which he had removed himself at Baggot Street Hospital or which had been supplied to him by his colleagues. He concluded: 'Investigations of this nature have opened a new door in the science of pathology and will lead, it is to be hoped, to an accurate knowledge both of the nature of malignant diseases, and of the diagnostic differences between them and affections of a benign character. Most important remedial improvements may be expected to rise out of such a consummation.'[3] One of Houston's notebooks, dated 1844-45, has been preserved in the library of the Royal College of Surgeons. It contains original drawings of cancer cells, urinary deposits and so forth, with notes concerning the patients.

Houston was a member of the Dublin Pathological Society and he also contributed a number of papers to medical literature, including his famous paper describing the rectal valves, permanent folds in the wall of the rectum. In this paper, which he wrote in 1830, he enumerated the reasons why it was important to appreciate their existence and he concluded by remarking:

> There is still another more weighty reason why the surgeon should bear in mind the existence of these folds, that he may not mistake them for strictures in the gut, a mistake which it is to be feared has often happened

to those who have reported such numerous cases of this disease, and which, by leading them to the frequent practice of bougies, many have brought on the very malady which these instruments were intended to remove.[4]

He died in 1845 at the age of forty-three, following a stroke during a clinic at the City of Dublin Hospital.

Another major advance of this period was that of subcutaneous or hypodermic therapy, introduced when the Dublin surgeon Francis Rynd became the first doctor to inject medication beneath the skin. Born in Dublin in 1811, Rynd received his medical education at the Meath Hospital where he was apprenticed to Sir Philip Crampton, one of the first six presidents of the Pathological Society. Crampton had been elected a fellow of the Royal Society for his description of a muscle in birds' eyes, published in 1813 in the *Annals of Philosophy*. He was also one of the founders of the Dublin

11.2   John Houston (1802-1845)
When he lectured to the Surgical Society of Ireland in 1844 on the use of the microscope in pathology, his *subject was so new to his audience that he had to begin with a description of the cell.*

Zoological Society. A skilful surgeon, he improved the operative procedures for cleft palate. The historian Cameron ranked him as one of the greatest surgeons of his time. A very able teacher, he took a particular interest in Rynd. As a student, however, Rynd had many interests outside medicine and spent much of the time fox hunting when he should have been on the wards. Despite this, Crampton recognised his ability and encouraged a colleague, Professor William Porter, to take the erring student in hand. Rynd did not disappoint Crampton. He became an able surgeon and eventually joined the consulting staff of the Meath Hospital. In 1849 he published a book on diseases of the urinary tract, entitled *Pathological and Practical Observations on Stricture and some other Diseases of the Male Urethra*. He dedicated the book to Crampton with the words:

> I am anxious to embrace this opportunity of giving public testimony to the untiring zeal with which you have always sought the advancement of the surgical profession and to those great talents and varied acquirements which have been uniformly employed in the cultivation and diffusion of scientific knowledge.[5]

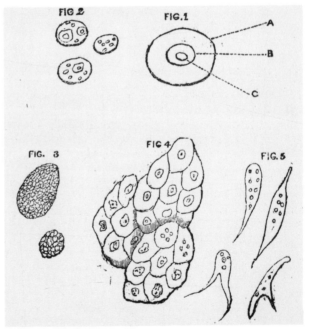

11.3 An illustration from Houston's paper 'On the microscopic pathology of cancer' (1844)

It shows a normal cell (fig. 1) and different types of cancer cells (figs. 2-5). Figure 3 shows cells from a carcinoma of the breast, from a patient in the South Dublin Union.

11.4   Francis Rynd (1801-1861)

Rynd, who gave the first hypodermic injection, was a surgeon at the Meath Hospital. He was also medical superintendent at Mountjoy Prison. He mixed in the upper echelons of society and it was said that 'few fashionable dinner parties of any consequence came off without his presence'.

Five years before the publication of this book, Rynd himself had made a major contribution to medicine when he gave the first hypodermic or subcutaneous injection. He invented a special instrument for this purpose, as the syringe had yet to be developed by Charles-Gabriel Pravaz of Lyons. On 18 May 1844, a woman suffering from intractable facial pain was admitted under Rynd's care at the Meath Hospital. Rynd decided to try to relieve her symptoms by injecting morphia in the region of the nerves:

> On the 3rd June a solution of fifteen grains of acetate of morphia, dissolved in one drachm of creosote, was introduced to the supra-orbital nerve, and along the course of the temporal, molar, and buccal nerves, by four punctures of an instrument made for this purpose. In the space of a minute all pain (except that caused by the operation, which was slight) had ceased, and she slept better that night than she had for months.[6]

Rynd also treated a man suffering from severe sciatica with subcutaneous morphine:

> He is unable to sleep from the pain, and quite unable to walk. He is much emaciated and the muscles of the limb are attenuated and wasted. He has been ill for three years, during which time he has been almost always confined to bed. He has been frequently treated for the disease with calomel, to produce salivation, cupping, blistering, leeching etc. all without salutary effect.[6]

On the 13 November the patient was given two injections of morphine along the course of the nerve and the pain immediately eased. Three days later the treatment was repeated with equal benefit. He left the hospital on 15 December, perfectly free from all pain and tenderness. The instrument developed by Rynd did not have a plunger and the fluid entered the tissues by the force of gravity alone. The technique of injecting medications beneath the skin was developed further by others and it is now used daily by doctors and nurses throughout the world.

Rynd died tragically in 1861. He was travelling into Dublin when his phaeton knocked down a woman accidentally; the woman was unharmed but during an altercation which followed Rynd collapsed and died. His biographer, Lambert Ormsby, thought his name would never be forgotten 'as the hypodermic needle is now so extensively used'.[7]

In 1834 St Vincent's Hospital on Stephen's Green was opened by the Irish Sisters of Charity. These nuns initiated some of the earliest nursing reforms in Ireland and Great Britain. At the time medical and surgical nurses were untrained and they did not wear uniform:

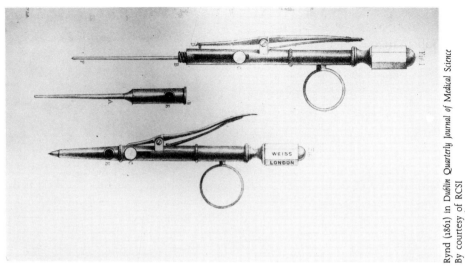

Rynd (1861) in *Dublin Quarterly Journal of Medical Science*
By courtesy of RCSI

11.5 Rynd's instrument for hypodermic
injections

The instrument was essentially a trocar and cannula. After penetrating the tissues the trocar was made to spring back out of the cannula by applying pressure on the lever at the side. The drug was then instilled through a small hole near the base of the cannula and allowed to gravitate into the tissues.

From Ormsby's *History of the Meath Hospital* (1892)

11.6 Nurses at the Meath Hospital in 1872   Hodgens (fever nurse), Spring (night nurse), Murray (surgical nurse), Brazil (accident nurse)

There was one to each ward, who was responsible for the patients by night as well as by day. These women were kind hearted and attentive, and I believe that — at least in the Dublin Hospitals — the patients were fairly well cared for and contented. In cases where patients were delirious, or required special watching at night, some respectable old woman of the charwoman class would be engaged to act as night nurse.[8]

Joseph O'Ferrall was the first doctor at St Vincent's Hospital. Born in Dublin around the year 1790, his mother belonged to an affluent family who disowned her when she adopted the Catholic religion. His father was not wealthy and the family received assistance from the priests in the Carmelite church in Clarendon Street. Until 1815, when he commenced the study of medicine, O'Ferrall worked as a clerk in a distillery for a small salary from which he contributed towards the maintenance of his brother and sister. He was apprenticed to Richard Carmichael and he studied at the Richmond School of Medicine. He obtained qualifications in both medicine and surgery. In 1841 he wrote a paper which is now recognised as a classic in the literature on ophthalmology. It contained a description of his operation for the enucleation of the eyeball. In the same paper he also described in detail the fibrous coat which invests the eyeball. However, unknown to O'Ferrall, a French doctor named Tenon had described the same structure just a few months before him and it is now known as Tenon's Capsule. O'Ferrall was an enthusiastic supporter of the Pathological Society from its foundation and contributed regularly to the meetings. In 1845 he collaborated with Dominic Corrigan to establish the *Dublin Hospital Gazette*, 'a two weekly periodical, entirely devoted to matters of practical and scientific import, unconnected with medical politics and uninfluenced by party feeling, jealousy or personal hostility'.[9] It concentrated mainly on lectures and clinical reports and it also carried regular descriptions of the presentations at the Dublin Pathological Society.

Robert Mayne, who was born in 1811 in County Meath and who studied at the School of Physic and the College of Surgeons, was another frequent contributor to the Pathological Society. He became a resident medical student in the Richmond Hospital where he cared for cholera victims during the 1833 epidemic. Mayne began to teach anatomy in the Richmond School in 1836 and soon became a popular lecturer. Although qualified in both surgery and medicine, the latter became his main interest. In 1845 he was appointed physician to the South Dublin Union. This was a large workhouse with a busy infirmary which provided medical services for the destitute poor as opposed to the 'genteel' poor who went to the voluntary hospitals. Despite his great workload Mayne took every opportunity to engage in

11.7   Francis Cruise (1834-1912)

Cruise, an enthusiastic endoscopist, wrote in 1865 that there was no portion of the human body into which an 'endoscope can be introduced in which it will not be found of service'. Pope Pius X conferred the Grand Cross of St Gregory the Great on him for his work on Thomas a Kempis.

clinical research and he published several papers including one on pericarditis (inflammation of the sac surrounding the heart) in the *Dublin Journal of Medical Science*. In this paper, which was translated into German and French, he pointed out that epigastric tenderness may be a feature of pericarditis, and for a time afterwards this was known as Mayne's Sign. In later years the historian Cameron wrote of Mayne: 'Although he undoubtedly deserves to be ranked amongst the greatest physicians which Ireland has produced, no one has ever made less parade of his talents.'[10]

Francis Cruise was another doctor with an inventive mind like Rynd. He was born in Mountjoy Square in Dublin in 1832 and he studied medicine in the School of Physic. He also studied under Corrigan in the Richmond Hospital. He recalled later his first impressions on meeting the great physician:

> Of commanding figure very like Daniel O'Connell, his face beamed with kindness, and his manner, if a trifle brusque was most fascinating. I put a question to him about a patient we had just seen in the hospital ward, and the painstaking manner in which he explained all I asked established a confidence never after shaken or forgotten.[11]

Cruise's health broke down at the end of his student career and he was advised to travel to the United States. There, in the backwoods, he became an expert rifle shot. He returned to Dublin and was appointed as a surgeon to the Mater Hospital when it was opened by the Sisters of Mercy in 1861. He became a member of the London College of Surgeons, but he was soon to switch from surgery to medicine. In 1859 he received the licentiate of the College of Physicians, five years later he was elected a fellow of the college and eventually he became its president. He relinquished his post as surgeon and was appointed consulting physician to the Mater. He wrote papers on many medical subjects but his most famous was his description in 1865 of the first effective cystoscope, an instrument for viewing the inside of the bladder. The cystoscope was first introduced by John Fisher of Boston in 1827. Later Antonin Jean Desormeaux of the Hopital Necker in Paris designed an endoscope and he became known as 'the father of cystoscopy'. However, the major drawback of all the early instruments was the poor illumination. Cruise improved on existing models by providing better illumination using the thin edge of the flat flame of a paraffin lamp. In an address delivered before the medical society of the College of Physicians in Ireland in 1866, William Stokes, who was the president of the college, singled out for special praise Cruise's contribution to endoscopy:

Originally described by Desormeaux, it was reserved for Dr Cruise to make the idea practically applicable; and so much has he made the instrument his own that, while Paris can claim to be the best place for the stethoscope, Vienna for the laryngoscope and Berlin the ophthalmoscope, Dublin is entitled to the honour if not of the discovery, at least of the application, of endoscopy .... Nothing can be more honourable to Dr Cruise, than the way he speaks of the researches of Desormeaux, claiming little more than an improvement in the illuminating power of the instrument. *But this is the great point*; and the light of Dr Cruise's endoscope, as compared with that of Desormeaux, is as daylight to twilight.[12]

By courtesy of RCSI

11.8 Cruise's endoscope, with its cystoscopic attachment   *The source of illumination, a paraffin lamp, is within the mahogany case. Cruise's own instrument is now preserved in the Royal College of Surgeons.*

113

Cruise designed the instrument for other uses as well as cystoscopy. There were attachments for examining the rectum, uterus, auditory meatus, nasal fossae, pharynx and larynx. He also had hopes that it might be adopted for investigation of the oesophagus and stomach. The instrument was exhibited at the Dublin meeting of the British Medical Association in 1867. The Cruise cystoscope was used in the London Lock Hospital and from there its use spread to several parts of England. It has been said of the instrument that it kept the practice of cystoscopy alive until it was superseded by the first modern-type endoscope with distal lighting which was developed by the German Nitze in 1877. Cruise himself used the instrument to study diseases of the urinary tract and was the first to describe the upward extension of the pathological process in gonorrhoea. Cruise's own endoscope is preserved in the College of Surgeons.

Having tried medicine and surgery, Cruise in his later years became keenly interested in psychiatry and the application of hypnosis to medicine. He was a man of broad culture and interests and was an authority on the works of the medieval spiritual writer Thomas a Kempis, author of *The Imitation of Christ*. Cruise translated many of his works and wrote a book about his life. This work was appreciated on the Continent and a street in Kempen was named after Cruise. Cruise also had a keen interest in music and he played the cello. He wrote some pieces for this instrument and he was a founder member of the Instrumental Musical Club which did much to promote classical chamber music in Dublin. Despite all these accomplishments, it was at the meetings of the medical club at Bohernabreena in the Dublin mountains that Francis Cruise really won his colleagues' esteem. At these meetings the medical men of the city relaxed and enjoyed themselves. Francis Cruise drew on his rifle-shooting experience in the backwoods of America, as one admiring colleague wrote: 'The distance from which he can shatter the neck of a champagne bottle without breaking its body is surprising, especially when it is considered that the shooting at Bohernabreena commences after the champagne bottles have been emptied'.[13]

CHAPTER 12

Dublin Lying-In Hospitals: Improving Obstetric Care

The Dublin school was famous not only for its high standard of medicine and surgery but also for the standards it achieved in obstetrics. The practice of midwifery at the Rotunda Hospital was an international attraction for students and doctors of the period. They came from England, America and the Continent, and there were even some from Russia. Robert Collins had sharply reduced the incidence of maternal death during his period as master obstetrician (1826-1833) by conducting strict regimes of personal and environmental cleanliness. Collins concluded that puerperal sepsis (infection after delivery) was a contagious disease and he introduced several measures designed to reduce the incidence of the condition.

A number of wards in the hospital were used in rotation as labour wards and each one was filled in turn by the new admissions. A midwife was placed in charge of each ward and neither patients nor midwife were allowed to move away from the ward. When the ward was full, no further admissions took place until all the patients had been discharged. Following this, the ceilings, the floors and the walls were treated with chloride of lime. All the windows, doors and other outlets were sealed and the empty ward was then filled with chlorine gas. This fumigation was continued for twenty-four hours. The straw in the mattresses was burnt and the mattress covers, blankets and bed linen were washed. Doctors and midwives had to wash their hands before delivering a baby and no student was allowed to attend the maternity hospital whilst involved in anatomical dissections. These measures were so successful that there was no fatality from puerperal sepsis in the hospital during the last three years of Collins' mastership. He maintained that puerperal fever arose from a local cause and not, as many surmised at the time, from something noxious in the atmosphere. Collins' book on midwifery, which was published in 1835, brought his work to the notice of others who were involved in the same area on the Continent. In the obstetrical clinic of the Allgemeines Krankenhaus in Vienna, Wilde's friend Ignaz Semmelweis expressed his intention of working with Collins for an extended period at 'the Great Lying-In Hospital of Dublin'.[1] He actually took some English lessons with this in mind, but his unexpected appointment as assistant in the Vienna hospital in March 1847 compelled him to abandon the project. Nevertheless, his immense contribution to solving the problem of puerperal sepsis almost certainly owes something to Collins' work at the Rotunda. In 1847 Collins received the MD of Trinity College, *honoris causa*.

William Fetherston Montgomery, one of the vice-presidents of the Pathological Society of Dublin, was the first occupant of the chair of midwifery when it was established in the School of Physic in 1827. In 1837 he published his classic work entitled An *Exposition of the Signs and Symptoms of Pregnancy, the Period of Human Gestation and the Signs of Delivery*. This book was translated into several languages and it contained a description and illustrations of Montgomery's Tubercles, small glands in the areola surrounding the nipples which become more marked during pregnancy:

> The surface of the areola especially that part of it which lies more immediately around the base of the nipple, is studded over and rendered unequal by the prominence of the glandular follicles, which, varying in number from twelve to twenty, project from the sixteenth to the eight of an inch, and, lastly, the integument covering the part appears turgescent, softer, and more moist than that which surrounds it, while on both these are to be observed at this period, especially in women of dark hair and eyes, numerous round spots or small mottled patches of a whitish colour scattered over the outer part of the areola and for about an inch or more all round, presenting an appearance as if the colour had been discharged by a shower of drops falling on the part.[2]

Montgomery was not the first to describe these tubercles, also known as Morgagni's Tubercles, but the six beautiful hand-coloured illustrations in his book showing the changes at different stages of pregnancy were probably a major reason for the Montgomery eponym. Lombe Atthill, a master of the Rotunda later in the century, remembered Montgomery as a small but not insignificant-looking man who:

> had a great idea of his personal appearance, of which he was vain. He always wore a white tie, and a diamond stud in his shirt front. It was told of him

that he caused no little merriment at a dinner party — all the guests being medical men — where the conduct of a lady said to be fast was discussed, it being stated that her husband was very jealous of her. Montgomery took no part in the conversation for some time, but a pause occurring said, 'Well gentlemen, I don't believe one of those stories. Mrs — has been my patient for months past. I have seen her over and over again alone in her house and at mine, and I can assure Captain — never once showed the least jealousy of me'. At this time Montgomery was long past seventy and looked it.[3]

An American edition of Montgomery's book was published in 1857. He died in 1859 leaving behind him, according to the Viennese obstetrician F H Arneth, 'a name which is known and honoured wherever Midwifery is practised'.

Fleetwood Churchill succeeded Montgomery as professor of midwifery in the School of Physic in 1856. Churchill, a native of Nottingham in England where he was born in 1808, was also a very able man. After studying medicine in London, Edinburgh, Dublin and Paris he settled in Dublin where he built up a large obstetric practice. He wrote several very successful books on obstetrics and gynaecology but his best known work was *The Diseases of Children*, which was first published in 1849. It was subsequently translated into several languages including, it was claimed, Chinese.

On 14 November 1838 the inaugural meeting of the Dublin Obstetrical Society was held in the Rotunda Hospital and Evory Kennedy, who was at that time master of the hospital, gave the introductory address. In outlining the purposes of the society he said:

> The subjects determined upon for our investigation, in addition to parturition, are the structure, treatment, and diseases of females. The physiology of reproduction, with its comparative anatomy: foetal structures and physiology: infantile development and diseases, and that neglected but very necessary branch of our art — medical jurisprudence.[4]

Kennedy then went on to outline the rise of obstetrics as a speciality which meant that the obstetrician was 'as much in repute, as formerly he was the reverse'.[4]

In March 1851 Arneth, a former assistant in the great Lying-in Hospital of Vienna, visited Dublin as part of a study of maternity services in France, Great Britain and Ireland. On his return to Vienna in 1853 he wrote a book comparing the obstetric practice in the different countries he visited with that of Austria. The book contained very favourable references to Dublin medicine:

> One of the principal attractions of the Dublin school, which is so highly

esteemed on the Continent, and which has of late years, through Carmichael, Stokes, Graves and Corrigan, drawn so much attention to itself, is the great Lying-In-Hospital, which in the number of births is indeed inferior to our Institute, but about equals the Parisian Maternité and the establishment at Prague. The Dublin school of midwifery is, properly speaking, the only one of importance in Great Britain.[5]

A table which compared the maternal mortality of the three largest lying-in hospitals of Europe over a twenty-two year period showed the Rotunda in a very favourable light. In the Paris hospital it was 4.18 per cent, in Vienna it was 5.35 per cent, and in Dublin it was 1.34 per cent. The maternal mortality rate fell to one per cent during the seven-year mastership of Robert Collins. Arneth observed that the Dublin School constantly attracted English and American students.

The Danish government sent Professor Levy of Copenhagen to look at the lying-in hospitals of London and Dublin and to report on the teaching of obstetrics. Levy published his findings in the *Bibliothek for Laeger* in July 1847. Having criticised the opportunities for obstetric instruction in London he then wrote:

> As an extremely interesting contrast, I now rejoice to be able to conduct the reader to Dublin, where we not only find one of the largest and best lying-in institutions in Europe, but where, at the same time, instruction forms an essential part of the working of the obstetric establishments.[6]

Professor Levy described the Rotunda Hospital in detail and concluded:

> But the fruits of these efforts are not to be lightly esteemed; for here, not only have more than double the number of poor lying-in women yearly admitted into all the obstetric institutions of London taken together, been in the same space of time attended in one hospital, under equally favourable sanitary conditions, but a practical school has been maintained, in which in the course of time, several thousands of young physicians from all parts of England have received a practical obstetric education; and lastly an incontrovertible proof has been given to the world that a credulous pusillanimity has been at work, when, setting aside the interests of education and science, it has been said that a fearful mortality is inseparably connected with great lying-in hospitals.[6]

In 1858 two former assistant masters of the Rotunda, Edward Sinclair and George Johnston, published an account of the routine of the Rotunda hospital in their book *Practical Midwifery*. At that time there were 103 beds in the hospital and eleven wards. Nine of the wards were used in turn for the reception of women in labour and the other two were for

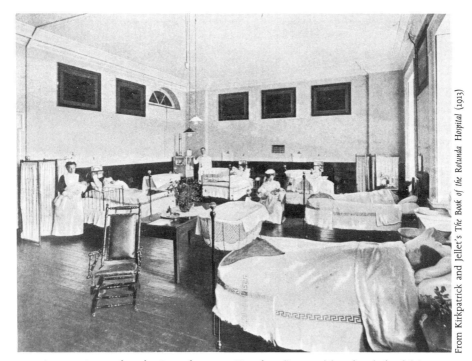

From Kirkpatrick and Jellet's *The Book of the Rotunda Hospital* (1913)

12.1 A maternity ward in the Rotunda Hospital in 1911

Note the cradles suspended at the end of each bed.

From Kirkpatrick and Jellet's *The Book of the Rotunda Hospital* (1913)

12.2 A group of students at the Rotunda in 1911

The Rotunda continued to draw students from abroad to study obstetrics and gynaecology long after the medical and surgical hospitals in Dublin had lost their places in the top rank of international medicine.

gynaecological problems. There were two small areas off each ward for patients whose condition warranted isolation. The hospital was particularly proud of its ventilation: 'the foul air being carried off by means of vent tubes which open upon the roof of the building, while a fresh supply is admitted from the corridors through the doors, all of which are perforated for that purpose'.[7]

The nine labour wards were filled in succession:

> As soon as the beds of the first were occupied with recently delivered women, labour was transferred to the second and so on. And it might be taken as an advantage, that each had its complement in less than forty-eight hours, generally in twenty-four. Now the patients, if sufficiently well, and if they desired it (for it was and, we believe, still is, perfectly optional with them), were discharged on the eighth day from their delivery, but under any circumstances, the ward in which they were delivered was emptied upon that day, and the patients, if not strong enough to be discharged, were removed to the convalescent room. Thus in eight days the ward first filled was emptied; and then a thorough cleansing and scouring was put in practice, and a free draught of air permitted through it, till just before it was again to be occupied with a fresh batch of labour patients; which was generally not until it had had two or three days' rest.[7]

When a woman was admitted she was assessed and any treatment deemed necessary was given. As soon as she entered the second stage of labour she was undressed and placed upon a low, narrow couch near the ward fireplace for delivery. She was allowed to rest on this couch for an hour after delivery and then she was 'carried horizontally to her bed, which was fresh and dry for her reception. Sometimes it was deemed necessary to wheel the couch to the side of the bed. The child, which had in the meantime been washed and dressed, was placed beside her, provided it was quiet and unlikely to disturb her'.[8]

After delivery the mother had to rest for several days and there were strict regulations with regard to visitors:

> Visitors were not allowed to see any patient till after the third day, and even then, as a general rule no female friends were admitted. Husbands could visit their wives every day after the third from delivery, and at all times, up to a reasonable hour, in accordance with their freedom from their ordinary occupations.[9]

In a footnote the authors explained that the rule excluding female visitors arose 'in consequence of the ill effects which frequently arose from the injudicious conversation of female visitors'.[9]

CHAPTER 13

Influencing North America

Many of the medical visitors who came to the capital went to the meetings of the Pathological Society of Dublin, and Dominic Corrigan certainly saw the society as a major attraction for these visitors:

> The Irish School of Medicine owes to it, I think I may say, the very high status which it holds at present throughout Europe and America. To it are paid the first visits of distinguished foreigners belonging to our profession, who come amongst us; and thus it has become the means of extending the fame of the Irish School of Medicine to every part of the civilised world. I believe I am not wrong when I state, that scarcely a meeting, since the commencement of the society, has been held, that has not been attended by foreigners of eminence from one part or another of the globe. At our last two meetings we have had visitors from classic Italy and majestic Greece.[1]

William Gibson, professor of surgery in the University of Pennsylvania, toured the major European medical institutions and described his findings in *Rambles in Europe* which was published in 1839 in Philadelphia. In concluding his observations on Dublin he wrote of 'its medical institutions, and equally celebrated medical men, which make it, beyond doubt, one of the best schools in Europe for the education of professional youth'.[2] Another American traveller, Dr Corson, described his impression of Dublin medicine in a work entitled *Loiterings in Europe* which was published in New York in 1848:

> One of the very best schools of practical medicine is doubtless that of Dublin. To be convinced of this, you have only to reflect upon the really valuable

additions it has made to the literature of the profession within the last 20 years. It is hardly necessary for me to mention the names of Colles, Graves, Stokes, Churchill, Marsh, Kennedy, Harrison, Jacob and others. They have become household words in medicine. Taken as a whole, you will probably meet with no practice abroad that will please you better than that of Steevens', the Meath, and the Lying-in-Hospital. Any medical friend going abroad to obtain knowledge, rather for use than show, or not quite familiar with French and German, I should advise to spend a very considerable portion of his time in the Irish capital.[2]

Robert Harrison, who succeeded Macartney as professor of anatomy and chirurgery in 1837, had a significant impact on American medical schools through his anatomical writing. Harrison was born in Cumberland in 1796 and he was sent to Trinity College Dublin to be educated. He was indentured to Colles in 1810 and he served as professor of anatomy and physiology at the College of Surgeons before his appointment in the School of Physic. In 1824 Harrison published his *Surgical Anatomy of the Arteries* in two volumes and it subsequently went through several editions. However, his most successful book was an anatomy textbook entitled *Dublin Dissector*. This work was used for more than fifty years as an anatomy textbook in medical schools on both sides of the Irish sea. It was issued as A *Textbook of Anatomy* in New York in 1848 and was the favourite students' manual in the American schools for many years.

Moreton Stillé, a graduate of the University of Pennsylvania, came to Europe for further medical training and spent some time with Graves and Stokes, for both of whom he acquired a high regard. Stillé was treated 'with marked kindness by Stokes, who evidently appreciated his good sense and the earnestness with which he devoted himself to his studies. In his last letter from Dublin, he mentions with pride that for two of his most precious and flattering letters of introduction to Dr Todd of London and Louis of Paris, he was indebted to Dr Stokes'.[3] Moreton Stillé became widely known in America for a book which he wrote with a leading lawyer, Francis Wharton, entitled A *Treatise on Medical Jurisprudence*. This was acclaimed as a 'masterpiece both of science and of literary style' and it was the first book on the subject which was written conjointly by a physician and a lawyer. Moreton's older brother Alfred also studied in Dublin and he was greatly influenced by Graves. Alfred Stillé had worked with the famous American physician W W Gerhard as a house physician in Philadelphia before going to Europe. Gerhard played a key role in establishing that typhoid and typhus were two separate diseases. Alfred Stillé had a very distinguished career when he returned to America from Europe and in

1864 he was appointed to the prestigious chair of medicine at the University of Pennsylvania. He was the first secretary of the American Medical Association and he became its president in 1867. Both of the Stillé brothers introduced the teachings of Graves and Stokes to Philadelphia.

Meredith Clymer was another physician from Philadelphia who studied in Dublin with Graves and Stokes. He was a grandson of George Clymer, one of the signatories of the Declaration of Independence, and when he returned to America he became a pioneer in the field of neurology. He was professor of nervous and mental diseases in Albany Medical College between 1871 and 1874.

Isaac Taylor and George Thompson Elliot were two Americans who studied at the Rotunda. Taylor pioneered the teaching of gynaecology in New York and he played a key role in obtaining a charter for Bellevue Hospital Medical College in 1861. Elliot was appointed professor of obstetrics at Bellevue and seven years after his appointment he published his book *Obstetric Clinic* in 1868.

From H Cushing's *The Life of Sir William Osler* (1940)

13.1   William Osler writing his famous textbook *The Principles and Practice of Medicine*

He dedicated this book to the memory of his teachers James Bovell and Robert Palmer Howard, both of whom studied under Graves and Stokes in Dublin. Bovell was a founder member of the Pathological Society of Dublin. Osler was very much in the mould of the great Irish physicians.

John Bassett of Huntsville Alabama, whom Sir William Osler has immortalised in his biographical study *An Alabama Student*, also brought favourable reports to America about the high standards of Dublin medicine. Osler, himself perhaps the greatest American physician, claimed links with the Irish school of medicine when he spoke at the bicentenary meeting of the School of Physic in the Dublin Mansion House in 1912:

> I owe my start in the profession to James Bovell, kinsman and devoted pupil of Graves, while my teacher in Montreal, Palmer Howard, lived, moved and had his being in his old masters, Graves and Stokes.[4]

James Bovell spent a few years in Dublin with Stokes and Graves. Bovell was born in the Barbados in 1817, where his father was an English banker. He went to England in 1834 and after a short stay at Cambridge he decided to study medicine in Guy's Hospital in London. He subsequently studied in Edinburgh and then went to Glasgow to take his first medical degree before travelling to Dublin. He was with Graves and Stokes during some of their most productive years. He was a founder member of the Pathological Society of Dublin and he attended the early meetings of the society. On 12 January 1839 he presented a case of 'Chronic abscess of the lung, with mortification of a portion of one of the ribs'. The session was chaired by Robert Harrison and among the other members who presented cases were Robert Adams and Robert Smith. Stokes was very impressed by Bovell's ability. When Bovell was recovering from typhus towards the end of his time in Dublin, Stokes predicted a brilliant career for him in the British Isles. However Bovell opted to cross the Atlantic again and he played a major role in developing medical teaching in Toronto.

Osler studied under Bovell for three years, between 1867 and 1870, and he was influenced greatly by him: 'Infected with the Aesculapian spirit he made me realize the truth of those memorable words in the Hippocratic Oath, "I will honour as my father the man who teaches me the Art" '.[5] Osler went to Montreal in 1870 where he entered the McGill Medical School and studied under Palmer Howard, the professor of medicine. Howard, from Osler's description, would appear to have absorbed many of the attributes of his great teachers in Dublin. Osler became one of Howard's senior students:

> Every lung lesion at the Montreal General Hospital had to be shown to him and I got my first hand introduction to Laënnec, to Graves and to Stokes and became familiar with their works. No matter what the hour, and it usually was after 10 pm I was welcome with my bag.[6]

In view of this influence it is not surprising that Osler, in a reply to an invitation to speak at the Meath Hospital in 1905, should state that 'both Graves and Stokes are among my special professional "friends" ''[7] During his time at McGill, Palmer Howard lost no opportunity for encouraging research in physiology and pathology and it was under his guidance that the medical school achieved a great reputation. It is significant that Maud Abbot, the first secretary and one of the principal driving forces behind the International Academy of Medical Museums (now known as the International Academy of Pathology) was a distinguished pathologist from McGill University. William Osler was at the first meeting of the academy in 1906.

Oliver Wendell Holmes of Harvard Medical School was another American doctor who thought highly of Graves. Holmes, like Semmelweis, made a major contribution in identifying the causes of puerperal fever. In an essay 'Scholastic and bedside teaching' in 1861 he wrote that Dr Graves of Dublin was "one of the first clinical teachers of our time".[8]

Irish doctors who emigrated from Ireland also contributed to the development of North American medicine. For example, Thomas Antisell, a graduate of Trinity College and assistant to Sir Robert Kane between the years 1839 and 1843, had to leave the country because of his involvement in the unsuccessful 1848 uprising. He escaped as a surgeon on an outgoing ship to America where he subsequently had a very successful career, becoming a professor at the University of Georgetown and between 1866 and 1871 chief chemist of the United States Department of Agriculture. Robert Kane made a major contribution to the Irish school by founding the *Dublin Journal of Medical and Chemical Science*. His son Francis also studied medicine. After a period of postgraduate work in Paris, Berlin and Vienna Kane was appointed as consultant physician to Jervis Street Hospital. In 1874 he left Ireland for San Francisco where he had a brilliant career, becoming professor of clinical medicine and pathology at the University of California in 1883. John Bryne was another who emigrated to America after working in a fever hospital during the famine. He was instrumental in founding a hospital, afterwards known as Long Island College Hospital. He became a leading gynaecologist and he was one of the original fellows of the American Gynaecological Society.

The Irish school of medicine exerted its influence on the development of American medicine, not only by direct contact between the doctors of both countries, but perhaps more importantly through the extraordinarily able books and articles produced from the pens of the Irish teachers. The works of Graves and Stokes in particular were most important and they were republished over many years. Their enthusiastic espousal of bedside teaching almost certainly influenced Harvard to offer students in the 1840s 'an opportunity of visiting all cases, and of observing the symptoms and treatment of each case ... by palpation, auscultation and percussion'.[9] Daniel Reisman, formerly professor of clinical medicine in Philadelphia, finished an essay in 1922 on the influence of the Dublin school on American medicine by concluding that:

> The practice of Graves and Stokes of having the students examine and follow the cases in the hospital became the American method. It is the one obtaining everywhere in this country today.[10]

By courtesy of RCSI

13.2 Wilde and Stokes share a bottle of beer

This photograph of the two friends was taken in the 1850s by Lord Justice Fitzgibbon and is one of the earliest of its genre.

CHAPTER 14

Medicine and the Arts

Apart from being an outstanding time for medicine, the fifty-year period between 1820 and 1870 has been described as a golden era for Irish art and science. Many of those associated with this era of achievement were members of the Royal Irish Academy which was founded in 1785. The objectives of this society were the advancement of science, the study of the country's antiquities, and research in what was then described as polite literature. The spirit of the academy was reflected in its motto 'We will endeavour', an aspiration shared by the Pathological Society of Dublin. It is not surprising that some doctors were members of both institutions. William Stokes rose to become president of the Royal Irish Academy, perhaps the highest honour for an Irishman of science or literature.

In the early years of the nineteenth century science like medicine was at a low ebb in Ireland. The Royal Academy appeared to be 'perishing of decrepitude' and its membership fell.[1] There were probably many complex reasons for this decline in the country's intellectual activities, but the most usual explanation given is the Act of Union between Ireland and England in 1801. This was William Stokes' explanation of the phenomenon:

> It is certain that the period from 1800 to 1821 was characterised rather by a kind of mental collapse than by activity. Such a result might naturally be expected when the political changes which the country had undergone are considered; and a period of at least one generation seemed requisite for the growth of those energies which would work out for Ireland her proper place, as an integral portion of the British Empire. The quarter of a century following 1821 is not the least remarkable period of our history, for it was then that a general movement in our departments of mental culture

commenced among us a movement giving good hope for the future of the country.[2]

Stokes attributed the new movement to reforms introduced by Bartholomew Lloyd, provost of Trinity College, which he claimed 'spread a new influence over the country as evidenced by the general advance in mathematical, physical, and natural science, and in the studies of literature and archaeology'. These reforms took place just before William Rowan Hamilton, the great Irish scientist, entered Trinity College in 1823. Hamilton was so brilliant as an undergraduate that he was appointed to a professorship in 1827, before he had actually graduated. He made several fundamental discoveries in mathematics. Today every physicist is familiar with the Hamiltonian Function, which is the typical starting-point for almost any type of dynamical calculation. He also made a major contribution to algebra through his discovery of quaternions. Hamilton was a very cultured man and was a close friend of both William Wilde and William Stokes. James MacCullagh, a native of County Tyrone, was another great mathematician who did remarkable work, particularly in optics. He suffered from severe depression at times and was a patient of William Stokes. MacCullagh's suicide in 1847 caused widespread shock and dismay. There were also many other outstanding men of science in Ireland at this time.

These scientists met the leading artists and poets of the period at the home of William Stokes in Merrion Square.

> The tie that bound William Stokes to these men was something more than ordinary friendship. Unversed as he was in the practical part, the technical work of the artist, and ignorant of higher mathematics, it was yet wonderful what sympathy and support these men derived from him, with what ardour his genius could reverberate to theirs. In the genial atmosphere he created around him, they seemed to live their fullest life, and those of them who died before him died beneath his care.[3]

Stokes was very interested in literature and he attended regular readings of Shakespeare's works at the homes of members of a Shakespearean society which had been inaugurated by Rev. Robert Perceval Graves, a cousin of the physician Robert Graves and a great-uncle of the poet of the same name. Robert Perceval Graves was a friend of William and Dorothy Wordsworth and he wrote a biography of William Rowan Hamilton. Other members of the Shakespearean society included John P Mahaffy and George Salmon, both of whom were to become provosts of Trinity College. Mahaffy remarked that when he:

> first came to know William Stokes his house had been for years the resort

of all the wit and all the learning which Ireland possessed. His fame brought all foreign visitors of literary note with introductions to see him.[4]

On Christmas Day Stokes made a special point of inviting foreign visitors to join his circle for dinner, to lessen the loneliness of their exile during the festive season. Often several different nationalities would be represented.

Stokes befriended the young John Pentland Mahaffy when the latter was 'a very lonely student in Trinity with no relations and very few friends in Dublin'. Mahaffy, who became a master of the art of conversation and tutor to Oscar Wilde, has left us a written account of his visits to Stokes' country residence at Howth:

> So I came to know him and talk with him, and learn from him perhaps more than many of the students in his hospital. We would constantly walk together over the heather and through the woods on the beautiful hill of Howth; and as he was urging me to study medicine, he used to stimulate my curiosity in that direction by conversations upon the treatment of fever, of nervous disorders, of chest complaints, in which all the large and interesting points were brought out, and all the unpleasant details skilfully omitted or subdued ... he never hurried himself in walking or talking, and often, in the midst of a summer tempest of rain, would stop deliberately, take out his snuff box, enjoy a large pinch of snuff, and then proceed to the point of the story, while the rain was streaming from our hats; for he never carried an umbrella, and used even to laugh at the genus of the umbrelliferae, as he called them.[4]

Mahaffy tells us that at dinner Stokes did not sit at the head of the table and carve like the traditional Victorian father. Instead he devoted himself fully to the conversation of his very brilliant and witty family circle. Mahaffy wrote a book about the art of conversation, The Principles of the Art of Conversation, and Oscar Wilde in a candid review regretted that his former tutor could not write as well as he could speak. Mahaffy curiously wrote something similar about Stokes, but in a more complimentary vein!

> I remember sitting beside him at dinner, when a scientific man was boring us with his talk. He turned to me, and said with emphasis: 'There is one golden rule of conversation — know nothing accurately'. He always observed this rule himself except where the interest actually lay in minute and careful description; then nothing could exceed the life-like picturesqueness of his language. There are men whose works speak their whole genius, and whom it is disenchanting to meet, for they have little personality outside their writings, which seem to absorb all that is great and good in them. But there are others whose published thoughts are as nothing compared with the influence they exercise upon those around them, and whose books are very

unsatisfying to those who have the privilege of their personal friendship. This is exceptionally true of William Stokes.[4]

The writers and artists who met at Stokes' home were pivotal figures in a new movement known as the Celtic Revival. The leaders of the movement saw an opportunity of restoring Ireland's self- respect by drawing attention to the great cultural achievements of the past. George Petrie, antiquary, artist and musician was one of the most important of these figures. The artist Frederic Burton was another who drew much of his inspiration from Irish antiquities and from contemporary life in Gaelic Ireland. He was a friend and travelling companion of Petrie and both shared the friendship of William Stokes. Burton's famous painting 'The Meeting on the Turret Stair' was inspired by a translation of an old Danish ballad by William Stokes' eldest son, Whitley, who became a distinguished celtic scholar. The poet Samuel Ferguson, a Belfast-born lawyer, was also a member of this group. He drew much of his inspiration from early Irish history and legends. One of his poems, 'Cromlech on Howth', was published in 1861 in an edition which was illustrated by Margaret Stokes, a daughter of the physician. The book was embellished with decorations from the ancient Book of Kells. Margaret shared her father's enthusiasm for Irish antiquities and went on several field trips with him, often being joined by Petrie and Burton and another keen antiquary, the Earl of Dunraven.

In 1857 a meeting of the British Association was held in Dublin. When it was over William Wilde organised an excursion to the Aran Islands on the west coast. Seventy sailed with him from Galway to Inishmore, where they studied the local antiquities including the ancient fort of Dún Aongus. The provost of Trinity presided and the group was addressed by Wilde. When the tour was over, Wilde, Stokes and their friends stayed behind for a fortnight. They rented a cottage and Stokes sent for his daughter Margaret. Burton painted the islanders whilst Petrie, with his manuscript music book and his violin, went from house to house collecting and recording the ancient songs and music of the islands. Stokes remembered the occasion vividly:

> Nothing could exceed the strange picturesqueness of the scenes which night after night were thus presented. On approaching the house, always lighted up by a blazing turf fire, it was seen surrounded by the islanders, while its interior was crowded with figures, the rich colours of whose dresses, heightened by the fire-light, showed with a strange vividness and variety, while their fine countenances were all animated with curiosity and pleasure. It would have required a Rembrandt to paint the scene.[5]

Stokes returned to the Aran Islands in 1867 with the Earl of Dunraven. He described this event in a letter to his eldest son, Whitley. They had taken a camera with them to the islands to record their findings and Stokes remarked that he found the expedition very hard work:

> But we have done great work, and we have measured, drawn and photographed almost every object of interest in the islands. I wish you had seen the group of natives that surrounded us in the great pagan fort on the middle island of Aran; nearly a hundred women and girls, all in their bright red dresses, sitting in a great circle round us, some at the base and some at the top of the great wall. Then we made a young man sing to us, and it was delightful to see how all the people enjoyed the song — an interminable Irish chant but very beautiful in its way.[6]

Stokes and Dunraven used a camera to record the antiquities of Galway, Mayo and Sligo, and the following autumn they recorded the antiquities of Kerry. A detailed account of the places visited on this occasion is given in the Earl of Dunraven's magnificent work, *Notes on Irish Architecture*, which was completed by Margaret Stokes after the death of the earl. According to the Celtic scholar Richard Henebry, it would not be possible to calculate the total influence of William Stokes on the movement which inspired the Celtic Revival.

By Courtesy of Trinity College Dublin

14.1 An Aran church in 1867
A photograph of St Benen's taken by Stokes and Dunraven during their visit to the Aran Islands to record the antiquities.

From Dunraven's *Notes on Irish Architecture* (1875)

Thomas Carlyle, the historian and philosopher, visited Ireland in 1849 and met Stokes at Merrion Square. Petrie and Burton were among the guests on that occasion, but the evening was not very successful. During the dinner Stokes' wife took umbrage at a remark made by Carlyle. The atmosphere did not improve as the evening progressed and according to Carlyle:

> Talk, in spite of my endeavours took on an Irish-versus-English character; wherein, as I really have no respect for Ireland as it now is and has been, it was impossible for me to be popular! Good humour in general, tho' not without effort always, did maintain itself. But Stokes, 'the son of a United Irishman' as I heard, grew more and more gloomy.[7]

Carlyle was not the only one to remark on Stokes' changes of mood. Athill Lombe, who was a student of Stokes, wrote:

> Stokes I was fortunate enough to have as a teacher, and to count as a kind friend in after-life — a man of great ability, but of varying moods. At one time he would be a genial and delightful companion, full of anecdote, and then, again, he would be quite the reverse, remaining even in genial company, quite silent.[8]

Stokes thought that Carlyle was one of the most boring men he had ever met, and his self-assertiveness, intolerance of opposition, and 'unconcealed contempt for everything and everyone in the country in which he was an honoured guest, struck Stokes as being as ill-mannered as it was low bred'.[9]

John Pentland Mahaffy remarked that Stokes' sympathies 'were far too keen and his nature far too sensitive, to admit of the equable cheeriness of vulgar minds'. According to Mahaffy, Stokes despised people who exhibited their patriotism by 'railing against England'.[10] However, although he was a staunch Tory all his life, he had:

> a curious contempt for the Saxons as he called them, from a social point of view. I mean of course the Saxons collectively, for no man had better or more revered friends in England. But if a plum pudding were put on the table, he would call it a low Saxon importation.[10]

It is hardly surprising that Stokes and Carlyle did not see eye to eye.

George Petrie was engaged in a major ordnance survey of Ireland and he enrolled some of the greatest Irish scholars to assist him in the task. He also employed the poet James Clarence Mangan as a clerk in his office. The Irish writers John Butler Yeats and James Joyce recognised Mangan as one of the most skilful Irish poets writing in English in the nineteenth century. 'My Dark Rosaleen' is probably his best known work. Mangan

By courtesy of the National Gallery of Ireland

14.2 *Anatomical Study* by John Hogan   *This early work (1820-23) in marble shows Hogan's*
dramatic sense of form and mastery of carving.

was a very eccentric person, who became dependent on drugs and in the end lived in great poverty. During the cholera epidemic of 1849 he was admitted to the Meath Hospital in a moribund condition. Thomas O'Reilly, a student in the Meath at the time, recalled the circumstances of Mangan's admission in a letter he wrote to Stokes' son in 1898 from St Louis Missouri: 'His miserable condition did not impress me, as the applicants for hospital admission at that time were almost all destitute, but what did impress me was the amazement of your father on seeing him.... With his characteristic humanity and sympathy, he turned to me and directed that Mangan should be placed in a private room clothed with flannels, and supplied with every necessary comforts at his expense.'[11] Despite the care which he received, Mangan died within a few days. Stokes asked his friend, the artist Frederic Burton, to come to the hospital where he drew the fine sketch of Mangan's head which is now in the National Gallery of Art.

Another member of the Pathological Society of Dublin who made a contribution to the celtic revival was the surgeon John Woodroffe. Woodroffe was born in Dublin in 1785 but spent the earlier part of his professional career in Cork, where he established his own private school. He allowed young artists to attend his dissecting sessions free of charge. Of these, Daniel Maclise the painter and John Hogan the sculptor achieved international recognition, the former in London and the latter in Rome. The works of both artists show the influence of the anatomical training which they received. In his biography of Maclise, O'Driscoll tells us that the artist occasionally dissected and that:

> this early discipline of his hand and eye in the science of anatomy, contributed very much to produce that marvellous facility and accuracy in delineating the human figure which imparts such a charm and grace to all his works.[12]

Maclise's best known works today are his two great frescoes in Westminster Palace — 'Wellington at Waterloo' and the 'Death of Nelson', and his magnificent painting on a historic theme 'The Marriage of Strongbow and Eva' which hangs in the National Gallery of Ireland. Hogan's best known works are his statues of O'Connell and Davis in the City Hall Dublin and his sculptures of the 'Dead Christ' in the Carmelite Church in Clarendon Street, Dublin, and the South Chapel in Cork. Early in his career Hogan carved a life-size female skeleton in wood which Woodroffe used during his lectures. It was considered sacrilege at the time to continue to display a skeleton indefinitely, thus depriving the victim of a proper burial. No one could object to a skeleton carved from wood.

Woodroffe moved to Dublin in 1841 where he became a surgeon to the

Charitable Infirmary in Jervis Street. Hogan also returned to Dublin from Rome in 1848 because of the political unrest on the Continent. He became a frequent guest at the home of William Wilde in Merrion Square. The last bust from Hogan's chisel was that of Robert Graves, and it is now in the Royal College of Physicians.

William Wilde used the experience which he had gained through several years of fieldwork to write *The Beauties of the Boyne and Blackwater*, editions of which are still appearing. He also wrote a book on the life of Jonathan Swift, which has remained a work of reference ever since. In 1864 he received the degree of MD *Honoris Causa* from Dublin University. Wilde shared an interest in literature with his wife Jane Francesca Elgee, whom he had married in 1851. She was a very talented young woman and although she was brought up in an atmosphere of unionism, she became involved with a group of nationalists who had formed a movement known as The Young Irelanders. She began to write very fiery poems for their newspaper *The Nation* under the pseudonym Speranza. Although Wilde admired her intellectual ability he stayed aloof from her politics.

Jane Wilde's own ardour for the nationalist cause cooled after the unsuccessful rebellion of 1848, which had been organised by her close associates William Smith O'Brien, John Mitchell and Charles Gavan Duffy. The Wildes then began to concentrate on their position in Dublin society and they moved to a larger house, number 1 Merrion Square. This Georgian square of tall, elegant, red brick houses was one of the most fashionable addresses in the city. Many members of the Irish school of medicine had houses there: William Stokes lived in number 5, Robert Graves in 84 and Dominic Corrigan in 92. The Wildes became celebrated for the number of dinner parties which they gave and the remarkable people who were invited. Usually about twelve people attended the dinners, but they also held receptions on Saturday afternoons at which there might be over one hundred guests. Charles Cameron, the medical historian, was a frequent guest at their table in the early sixties. Dr Thomas Beatty, an obstetrician who had the unusual distinction of being president of both the Royal College of Physicians and the Royal College of Surgeons was another frequent guest. He was also a founder member of the Pathological Society of Dublin. He had an excellent voice, as had another guest, Rev. Charles Tisdall. 'It was their custom to meet in Wilde's study and then to ascend the stairs slowly, singing a duet, to the drawing room.'[13]

In 1857 the Governor of Uppsala, Baron Robert von Kraemer together with his daughter, the writer Lotten von Kraemer, called on Wilde at Merrion Square. Many years later Lotten described the impression Wilde made on her:

> The noble figure is slightly bowed, less by years than by ceaseless work ... and his movements have a haste about them which at once conveys the impression that his time is most precious.... He carries a small boy in his arm and holds another by the hand. His eyes rest on them with content. They are soon sent away to play, whereupon he gives us his undisturbed attention.[14]

Baron Kraemer invited Wilde to Sweden and in 1862 he conferred the Order of the Polar Star on him. Wilde enjoyed wearing this Swedish decoration and the uniform that went with it, and members of the Irish Academy were instructed to call him 'Chevalier'.

Wilde was knighted in 1864 but his enjoyment of the new honour did not last long. In the same year, a woman with whom he had unwisely formed a relationship set out to ruin him. She was Mary Travers, a daughter of Dr Robert Travers, lecturer in medical jurisprudence at Trinity College. Wilde first met Mary Travers when William Stokes referred her to him for a professional opinion because of a hearing problem. Over a period of years Mary Travers became more and more demanding and eventually Wilde tried to end their relationship. She was infuriated and sought revenge by circulating a rumour that Wilde had assaulted her sexually. The whole affair led to an unseemly High Court action, when Mary Travers brought a civil action for libel against Lady Wilde and her husband because of a letter Lady Wilde had written to Mary's father about her activities. The Irish politician and barrister Isaac Butt, an old associate of Wilde's, acted for Miss Travers. The whole episode bore great similarities to the court case which years later would destroy the career of Wilde's son, Oscar. The jury found for Mary Travers and awarded her one farthing damages. Wilde did not have to enter the witness box.

Most of the medical profession supported Wilde during this very stressful period, the one notable exception being the *Dublin Medical Press* which was now edited by Archibald Jacob, a son of Arthur Jacob. This journal criticised Wilde for avoiding cross-examination and it concluded that 'Sir William Wilde has not satisfactorily refuted the charge of which he stands accused'.[15] On the other hand the Dublin correspondent of *The Lancet* congratulated Wilde on being 'acquitted of a charge as disgraceful as it was unexpected, without even having to stoop to the painful necessity of contradicting it on oath'.[16] Lady Wilde claimed that her husband had letters of support from most of the leading doctors in Dublin.

After the trial, Wilde took less interest in clinical work and he left the affairs of his hospital in the hands of his natural son, Henry Wilson, an able ophthalmologist whose book on the ophthalmoscope was the first to be written in the English language. Wilde now spent much of his time at Moytura, the country home which he erected in 1865 on the shores of Lough Corrib, and he wrote a book on the history and antiquities of the area. He maintained his friendship with William Stokes and other leading members of the Dublin medical establishment. Wilde belonged to a dining club called the Medico-Philosophical Society. According to the rules of the society, each member in his turn had to entertain the other members at his home:

> The dinners to be given in rotation by the members, but any member, who may attain to a position of honour or of considerable emolument to have the privilege of giving an extra dinner to the society.[17]

Apart from Wilde, there were many distinguished doctors in the society including Stokes, Adams, Crampton, Rynd and Beatty. Early in June 1868 Wilde invited Stokes and several other members of the society to spend a few days with him at Moytura. Dr Beatty, the secretary, has left us a detailed account of this visit in the minutes book of the society. The party met at Broadstone railway station where a carriage had been reserved for them. The train journey to Galway took six hours and:

14.3 Moytura

'From the hill of Tonlegee, overlooking this latter locality, was taken the accompanying view of Moytura House, the residence of the Author, erected in 1865, and so called after the ancient battle-field on which it stands, with Benlevi Mountain in the distance and Lough Corrib in front. The tower with the flagstaff stands within the enclosure of one of the ancient cahers of the battle-field. This house commands a magnificent prospect to the west, south and east and can be seen from most parts of the middle lake.'

From Wilde's Lough Corrib (1867), p 157

By courtesy of Trinity College Dublin

the sides of the party were in a more tender condition on their arrival at Galway than they were leaving Dublin. Some might imagine that this was owing to the concussion of the railway motion but it has been suggested by some eminent physiologists that laughter had something to do in the production of the phenomenon.[17]

At Galway they were met by a local doctor who had an omnibus ready to convey them to his house. There they were entertained to a sumptuous luncheon with liberal libations of hock and champagne before they left to board the Eglington Steamer to travel to Moytura.

> Half an hour before we reached the landing place the flag of the Chevalier was seen floating majestically from the top of a high tower in the grounds of Moytura that bordered the Lough.[17]

The 'Chevalier' met them on the pier and they were escorted up to the 'chateau'. They were shown to their bedrooms where Wilde had thoughtfully pinned a label with a name on the pillow of each bed as 'he knew the sherry, Madeira, hock, champagne and claret were excellent and above all that the poteen was irresistible.'[17] Soon all the party was enjoying roast salmon and beef, seated 'at the well known oval table brought from Dublin for the occasion'. After the dinner:

> All restraint was flung into Lough Corrib and toasts and speeches, songs and fun and frolic and poteen punch were indulged into a very late hour, and though diligent enquiry has been made by the secretary, he has not been able to find any one of the party, including himself, who can tell at what hour they went back to bed.[17]

Remarkably, on the following day all members of the party were fresh as larks and there was not one headache amongst them. They explored the countryside and met the local gentry at another lively banquet in the evening. Early next morning they had to board the steamer at Cong. It was a dull grey morning and as they:

> drove down the avenue we perceived that the flag of the Chevalier was hoisted half mast on the top of its lofty tower, a touching though silent demonstration of the feelings of our kind and generous host.[17]

During the following years Wilde continued his interest in archaeology and he revised *Lough Corrib* for a second edition. In 1873, just three years before his death, his contribution to archaeology was acknowledged when he was presented with the Cunningham Gold Medal, the highest award of the Royal Irish Academy.

CHAPTER 15

The Death of Graves

Robert Graves resigned his position as physician to the Meath Hospital in 1843, at the age of forty-six. In a letter to Francis Rynd, who was the secretary of the medical board at the time, he gave his reasons:

> I have been induced to take that step in consequence of finding that I could no longer discharge my duties to the patients and pupils in a satisfactory manner. You will much oblige me, my dear Rynd, by expressing the deep sense of gratitude which I feel for the cordial co-operation I always received from my colleagues during the period of twenty-two years I have been physician to the hospital.[1]

When the letter was received by the medical board, William Stokes and Francis Rynd were instructed to call on Graves to ask him to reconsider his resignation. Graves declined and he was succeeded by Dr Catchcart Lees, who had been physician to the South Dublin Union and was a member of the Dublin Pathological Society. Graves maintained a professional connection with the Coombe Maternity Hospital (established in 1826) and with the Adelaide Hospital (established in 1834). The regius professorship of physic fell vacant in 1845 and there were two candidates for the chair — Robert Graves and William Stokes. It was unfortunate that the two luminaries of Irish medicine should have had to compete for the one chair. William Stokes was the successful candidate, receiving four votes against Graves' three. They competed again in 1849 for the presidency of the Royal College of Physicians. Graves had already held the post in 1843 and on this occasion Stokes was elected. Graves was elected a fellow of the Royal Society in 1849. He was an honorary member of many of the learned societies of Europe, including those of Berlin, Vienna, Tübingen, Bruges and Montreal.

Despite the competitive element in their relationship, Graves and Stokes maintained a warm friendship throughout their lives. In 1843 Graves recalled the difficulties and the prejudice which he had to face when he first introduced bedside teaching:

> I remember perfectly well having only two practising pupils in one class, but I was not discouraged; and although we have had many numerous classes in the Meath Hospital, I doubt if any of them contained more talent and worth than was shared between my two pupils, Dr Townsend and Dr Stokes. Since the latter, from being my pupil, has become my colleague, he has evinced the most indefatigable zeal in co-operating with me in instructing the pupils of the Meath Hospital; and I am sure he joins with me in testifying the constant gratification we have received from observing that our efforts have been so far successful, that no season elapses without bringing under our immediate observation several pupils whose diligence, zeal and moral worth insure our warmest approbation. Many of these gentlemen have already distinguished themselves, — and will always carry with them the best wishes of myself and my colleagues.[2]

According to tradition, Graves' practice declined for some years before his death and medical historians have failed to find a reason for this. Cameron, writing in 1886 in his *History of the Royal College of Surgeons in Ireland*, stated that it was 'not because he was becoming old (for he died in the prime of life) but for some reason difficult to understand'.[3] Graves drew a curtain around his private life and as a consequence very little was known about family affairs in 4 Merrion Square. He prohibited the publication of any personal details in biographical sketches written during his lifetime. A pamphlet 'Some Notes on The Graves Family', which was intended for private circulation only, was published in 1889. It is apparent from this book, which was written by Hercules Graves MacDonnell, that Robert Graves must have experienced great personal suffering. He was married three times. His first wife, Matilda Jane Eustace, whom he married in 1821, was his first cousin. She died in 1825 leaving a daughter Eliza who died in 1831. He married Sarah Jane, daughter of a distinguished scholar and churchman, Dr John Brinkley, in 1826. She died a year later leaving a daughter who died in childhood. Graves married for the third time in 1830, when he was thirty-three years old. It was not until 1960, when his grand-daughter Nora Robertson wrote her biography *Crowned Harp*, that we got any information about Graves' home life. What she reveals suggests that Graves may have had good reason for reticence.

Graves' third wife, Anna Grogan of Slaney Park, Baltinglass, was a most 'conventional and decorous' woman and was very aware of social status.

Robert Graves belonged to a family whose members were renowned for their intellectual achievements. However, Anna had 'no intellectual interests, but a nice taste in *objets d'art*, which she collected with skill. She was disparaged as a worldly ignoramus by the learned Graves family, whose marriages were still enlarging their cultural scope'.[4]

In Ireland during the last century there was a strictly observed social order. At that time everyone knew their place in this order and all were aware of those who were in the top ranks. Before her marriage Anna Grogan, as a member of a 'county family', would have belonged to the higher echelons of this order. After her marriage it was a constant irritant to her that Robert Graves was a doctor. According to her grand-daughter 'she worked the eminence to which he rose so adroitly that the Lord Lieutenant and his Lady actually dined with them in Merrion Square. Still, she could not feel that this imprimatur was as enduring as founding a country seat and, before his death, she persuaded him to buy Cloghan Castle, a distinctive Norman keep by the Shannon, near Banagher'.[5] Graves did not survive very long after the purchase of the property. He died from a very painful disease of the liver on 20 March 1853.

Graves' death made a big impact on many members of the Irish school. William Wilde was preparing his classic work on aural surgery at the time. There had been a strong friendship between the Graves and Wilde families

15.1 Cloghan Castle, Banagher, County Offaly

Before being acquired by Graves, Cloghan Castle was the residence of Garret O'Moore, High Sheriff of Kings County (now County Offaly) in 1841. Graves' wife continued to live at Cloghan after his death. She was a harsh landlord and had to have constant police protection.

and Wilde himself was only ten when he first met Graves. Wilde paid a tribute to Graves in his book:

> It is with heart felt sorrow I have now to speak and write of Dr Graves in the past tense. Since my previous notice of this distinguished physician, the science of medicine at large, and the Irish Nation in particular, have experienced a loss which is not likely to be replaced in the lifetime of the present generation; and the author has been deprived by death of one of his earliest, firmest and best friends.[6]

Ten years after Graves' death a collection of his essays was published under the title *Studies in Physiology and Medicine*. The volume was edited by William Stokes who also contributed a biographical sketch on Graves in which he paid homage to his life long friend. As one of their contemporaries recalled, the personal relationship between Graves and Stokes had been a major factor in the success of the Irish school:

> Colleagues in office, they were animated by the same noble ambition — to spread the reputation of the Irish School of Medicine over the civilised world, and to uphold the honour and dignity of the profession that they loved — an ambition unsullied by jealousy or personal considerations as to rival merits, which so often mars the finest human characters.[7]

CHAPTER 16

Success for Stokes

After the publication of his work on diseases of the respiratory system in 1837 Stokes concentrated his clinical research on disorders of the heart. Over the following years he published several papers on heart disease in the *Dublin Quarterly Journal of Medical Science*. These formed the basis of his book *Diseases of the Heart and the Aorta*, which was to prove a milestone in the evolution of cardiology. The book was published in 1854 and was dedicated by the author to his brother-in-law, Robert Smith. Stokes at this time was regius professor of medicine and Smith was the professor of surgery in the School of Physic. Stokes wrote:

> In the composition of this work, while contending with difficulties inseparable from an attempt to combine the results of many years of labour, I have always been consoled by the thought that in dedicating it to you, I should be enabled to bear testimony not alone to the value of your contributions to Medical Science, but also to the signal benefits which your teaching and example have conferred upon the School of Surgery in this country.[1]

Stokes drew on the experience of many members of the Irish school of medicine when writing his book. This made the work particularly valuable as many of the physicians and surgeons of the school, such as Graves, Corrigan, Adams and Mayne, and in particular Stokes himself, had concentrated much of their efforts on diseases of the heart and circulation. Snellen in his *History of Cardiology* (1984) states that Stokes' treatise on the heart contains many conclusions that are surprisingly advanced and which agree with other writings of a much later date.

Shortly after publication, Stokes' book was translated into several different languages. Doctor J Lindwurm, in his introduction to the German edition

(1855), wrote that the views of the author were at variance with those prevalent in Germany at the time and that doctors should now choose between the German and Irish approach to cardiology. Contemporary German works on cardiology placed great stress on the physical signs, such as the presence or absence of murmurs. Stokes on the other hand stressed the importance of assessing the functional ability of the heart and he also emphasised the importance of differentiating between organic and inorganic murmurs:

> The two great practical points to be attended to are, first, whether the murmurs really proceed from an organic cause, and next, what is the vital and physical condition of the muscular portion of the heart; for it is upon these points that prognosis and treatment must really depend.[2]

Healthy individuals were being advised to live as invalids at the time, simply because their physician had heard a heart murmur. The pragmatic approach advocated by Stokes would save many from such a fate.

Stokes' book also contained his own description of the pattern of respiration now known as Cheyne-Stokes Breathing:

> A form of respiratory distress, peculiar to this affection, consisting of a period of apparently perfect apnoea, succeeded by feeble and short inspirations, which gradually increase in strength and depth until the respiratory act is carried to the highest pitch of which it seems capable, when the respirations, pursuing a descendant scale, regularly diminish until the commencement of another apnoea period. During the height of the paroxysm the vesicular murmur becomes intensely puerile.[3]

Stokes' first description of this phenomenon was published in the *Dublin Journal of Medical Science* in 1846 and referred to the original report of John Cheyne. It was Professor Ludwig Traube of Berlin who first termed it the Cheyne-Stokes Phenomenon; before that it had been known as ascending and descending respiration. Stokes had some revolutionary ideas for his time on the treatment of heart disease. He advocated that the patient must 'pursue a system of graduated muscular exercises; and it will often happen that, after perseverance in this system, the patient will be enabled to take an amount of exercise with pleasure and advantage, which at first was totally impossible.'[4]

The cardiac arrythmia, known as paroxysmal supraventricular tachycardia, was also described for the first time and this section was reproduced by Ralph H Major, professor of medicine at Kansas School of Medicine, in his book *Classic Descriptions of Disease*, with the first of several editions being published in 1932.

Sir William Hale-White of Guy's Hospital summed up the influence which Stokes' two major works had on medical practice in his book *Great Doctors of the Nineteenth Century*:

> In the nineteenth century three books appeared, one written by Laënnec, two by Stokes, which are the foundation of our knowledge and every-day diagnosis of diseases of the chest. Before Laënnec physicians generally did not or would not examine the chest; they speculated .... Readers of Stokes must not turn away from him when they come across opinions which experience has not confirmed; he was a pioneer, most pioneers make mistakes, he made very few, which count as nothing in comparison with the truths he enunciated as a result of his own observations and which he drove home with a terseness and clarity not surpassed by any other writer. The enormous advance made in medicine from 1820 to 1870 was in diagnosis and morbid anatomy; in this advance no one played a greater part than Stokes.[5]

Stokes' interests in medicine ranged over a wide area. He was particularly keen on promoting preventive medicine or, as it was known then, state medicine. In an address delivered before the University of Dublin in 1872 Stokes spoke of his hopes for the future:

> A time may come when the conqueror of disease will be more honoured than the victor of a hundred fights. The time may come when no man for his own ends or profit will be permitted to damage the health or the well-being of his neighbour or of his servant, nor the prisoner have to suffer through the ignorance or the indifference of his jailer; while the emigrant with his loved ones will be protected from disease as he expatriates himself from the land of his birth.

> The gifts to man from heaven — pure air, pure water, bright light, and wholesome food — will be more freely shared in, and the moral and physical evils of over-crowding, and the consequential guilt, the shame, the pestilence, will disappear.

> The artisan will be taught the dangers of his particular calling and — so far as law and public opinion go — be protected from them, whether he labours in a hot room, amid the roar of machinery or deep in the earth, where he has to work in passages, carved by himself, of little more than two feet in height, inhaling the smoke of gunpowder and particles of silex till his working life comes to an untimely and miserable end.[6]

Eventually, as a result of his exertions, Trinity College introduced the first diploma in state medicine in 1871. State medicine included forensic, psychological as well as preventive medicine. One of the results of Stokes' efforts to promote the study of preventive medicine was the establishment of the Dublin Sanitary Association. In the theatre of the Royal Dublin Society (RDS) Stokes delivered one of a series of lectures on sanitary science. In this lecture he dealt mainly with the causes and origin of epidemic disease, contagion, sanitary engineering and sanitary law. The lecture drew a huge audience and 'all present knew they were listening to one who by fifty years labour among the poor of Dublin was well fitted to instruct them in dealing with these questions'.[7]

16.1   The Royal College of Physicians of Ireland, from a wood engraving in the *Dublin Builder* (1862)

The foundation stone was laid by the Lord Lieutenant, the Earl of Carlisle, on 7 July 1862. In an address to the assembly, Corrigan pointed out that the School of Physic together with the College of Surgeons and the private medical schools attracted to Dublin about 1000 students from Europe, America and India.

By courtesy of RCPI

CHAPTER 17

Corrigan Enters Politics

Dominic Corrigan shared William Stokes' concern for the conditions of the poor and deprived. Unlike Stokes, however, Corrigan became actively involved in politics. After the famine, Corrigan's fortunes began to improve. He was appointed physician-in-ordinary to Queen Victoria in Ireland, the first time such an honour had been granted to a Catholic. In 1849 Trinity College bestowed on him a doctorate of medicine.

The College of Physicians, however, refused Corrigan an honorary fellowship, and the physicians appeared to be determined to exclude him. Then in 1855, at the age of fifty-three, Corrigan did a remarkable thing; he sat with the final-year students for the college's basic graduating examination, the Licentiate. He was successful, so there could now be no further justifiable reason for his exclusion. He was admitted to the fellowship the following year. Just twelve months later William Stokes proposed him for the presidency. Corrigan was successful in the subsequent election, defeating his opponent Sir Henry Marsh by eighteen votes to three. Corrigan became one of the most outstanding presidents of the College of Physicians and held the office for five successive years — an achievement not equalled since.

The fellows held their meetings in Sir Patrick Dun's Hospital as they did not have a hall of their own. Corrigan decided that his priority as president was to obtain an independent and suitably dignified hall for their transactions. He set about this with determination and on 7 July 1863 the foundation stone for the new college in Kildare Street was laid. Corrigan also ensured that no distinguished physician could be excluded from the fellowship on the grounds that he was not a graduate of Trinity, Oxford or Cambridge.

Corrigan had the satisfaction of enjoying an international reputation during his lifetime. He often visited the major hospitals in the capital cities of Europe. On one occasion he joined a group of French doctors and students on a ward round in a Parisian hospital. They came to a case which one of the doctors described as 'Maladie de Corrigan', and then, remembering he had an Irish visitor, the doctor asked him if he knew Corrigan of Dublin. 'C'est moi, Monsieur', Corrigan replied. He was then greeted with great enthusiasm and was led away to a lecture theatre where he was presented to the staff and students of the hospital.

Corrigan had a strong sense of dignity and could be very self-important at times. It has been suggested that this may have been an over-compensation for the restrictions to which Catholics were still subject, long after the Emancipation Act of 1829. He walked out of a banquet in the Mansion House, the residence of the Lord Mayor of Dublin, in 1864 when he found that he had not been seated at the high table. The lord mayor wrote to apologise and said the difficulty arose because of an unprecedented attendance by the nobility. In his reply Corrigan said that he did not see it as a personal affront, but that it had been the custom to place the president of the College of Physicians in a high place and that no profession merited the compliment more than his.

This sense of dignity may also have been a factor in Corrigan's rejection of overtures made to him by the English churchman Cardinal Henry Newman in 1855 when Corrigan was asked if he would accept the first chair of medicine and become dean of the faculty in the new Catholic university which Newman was planning for Dublin. Corrigan had incurred the displeasure of some of the hierarchy by accepting a place on the senate of Queen's University, which was established in 1845 with three constituent colleges at Cork, Galway and Belfast. These colleges were intended to be non-sectarian. They were denounced as 'Godless Colleges' by the Irish Catholic leader Daniel O'Connell. Corrigan, as he would show later when he became a member of parliament, did not favour sectarian education but he may also have feared that if he accepted Newman's offer, he might then have been rejected publicly by some members of the hierarchy.

The physician Francis Cruise recalled that Corrigan would not tolerate lack of consideration. On one occasion Cruise asked Corrigan to see a patient with him and in due course they met at the home of the sick person on a very cold day. After the bedside examination they were shown into a fireless drawing-room. Corrigan told Cruise that he would not consult there. He opened the door of another room where the family was standing around a big fire and said, 'Let us exchange rooms'. After the consultation he called the family back. They were relieved to find that the prognosis was favourable. 'Now,' he said, smiling, 'Do you think Dr Cruise and I could have done justice to the case if we had been left perishing in the other room?'[1]

In the same year that Dominic Corrigan was elected president of the College of Physicians he was also elected to the presidency of the Dublin Zoological Society. Corrigan was very interested in nature and devoted much of his time to the affairs of this society. He had his own aquarium at his country residence in Dalkey. This residence, called Inniscorrig, was built in Tudor style and over the doorway Corrigan placed a granite bust of himself wearing a laurel wreath. He bred tropical fish and reptiles in

17.1   The entrance of Inniscorrig

The house on Coliemore Road, Dalkey, is beautifully situated overlooking the sea. The bust of Corrigan, encircled by a laurel wreath, can be seen over the door.

149

the aquarium and some of these he presented to the Zoological Gardens. Apart from Corrigan a number of other well known doctors served on the Council of the Dublin Zoological Society, including William Wilde and Samuel Haughton.

Haughton was the registrar of the School of Physic and he had a most unusual career. His early interests were in geology and mathematics and he was elected a fellow of the university. At that time fellows in Trinity had to take Holy Orders, as had the fellows at Oxford and Cambridge, so Haughton was ordained. In 1851, at the age of thirty, he was appointed to the chair of geology. He published several substantial papers on mathematics and the scientific merit of his work was rewarded in 1858 when he became a fellow of the Royal Society. In 1859 he decided to study medicine and, without relinquishing his chair, he became a student in the School of Physic. Two years later he became a pupil in the Meath Hospital.

Haughton developed a particular interest in limb movement and the actions of muscles, an area which was also amenable to mathematical analysis. He did an extensive series of dissections on the muscles of many animals including the ostrich, emu, cassowary, pheasant, alligator, crocodile, hedgehog, monkey, llama, sloth, leopard, jaguar, tiger and lion. In all cases he made careful measurements of the muscle dimensions and the length of the tendons. This work led eventually to his book *The Principles of Animal Mechanics*, which was published in 1873. Here Haughton stated that the muscular mechanism is so arranged that its work is carried out with the minimum of muscular contraction. This he called the 'principle of least action'.

Haughton also used his knowledge of mathematics and anatomy to make the hanging of criminals more humane. At that time condemned men often died a slow and agonising death by strangulation, over fifteen to forty-five minutes, as it was common to allow the victim to drop just two or three feet for fear of decapitation. Haughton suggested that a longer drop would dislocate the joints at the junction of the vertebral column and skull and so cause instantaneous death. He worked out a formula based on the weight of the criminal which gave the length of the drop required to produce instant death. His formula was adopted widely and is now known as Haughton's Drop.

Haughton was a man of liberal views and he was primarily responsible for the 1867 Act (The School of Physic Act Amendment Act) which removed the restriction that professors of the School of Physic must be Protestants. When the magnificent statue of Corrigan by the sculptor J H Foley was unveiled in the College of Physicians by William Stokes in 1869, Haughton said: 'He felt proud that there was at least one institution, the College of Physicians, where apart from politics or religion, they could pay a tribute to genius and distinguished ability.'[2]

The unveiling of his statue in the College of Physicians did not mark the end of Corrigan's career. He was still very involved in medical and academic politics and was a commissioner on lunatic asylums. He was a member of the senate of Queen's University and the General Medical Council. He had been knighted by Queen Victoria in 1866 and three years later, at the age of sixty-seven, he successfully sought election to the House of Commons at Westminister. One of the main issues which he championed during his parliamentary career was non-sectarian university education. His stand on this issue eventually brought him into conflict with the Catholic hierarchy even though he had been an outspoken champion in Westminster of the rights of Catholics to higher education.

Apart from some small amount of private work Corrigan's involvement in the practice of medicine ceased when he became a member of parliament. He looked back with pride at his own achievements and those of the Dublin school of medicine. A contemporary report shows that when speaking at a debate in 1869 he referred to the poor state of medicine in Dublin at the beginning of the nineteenth century:

> There was a medical school connected with Trinity College attended by about forty students. The Royal College of Surgeons was then struggling into existence. He went to Edinburgh under the impression that medicine would not be taught at home. To what lengths had the Dublin School risen in a few years? It had risen to an eminence which had no parallel elsewhere in their time. Its name had reached America and every part of Europe.[3]

Corrigan retired from active politics in 1873 when the prime minister, William Gladstone, dissolved the parliament. Five years later when he retired from the Board of Superintendence of the Dublin Hospitals the press praised his great contribution to Irish medicine and observed that: 'it has been his rare good fortune to taste the perfect assurance of immortality — to see his statue set up among the monarchs of his profession, and hear his name quoted as part of the world's property in the highest of the schools'.[4]

Corrigan became ill at his residence in Merrion Square on 30 December 1879. Dr Francis Cruise came to see him and diagnosed a stroke. Corrigan lingered for a further month, remaining lucid to the end. With great loyalty and affection, Cruise slept in an adjoining room during those last weeks, in case he should be needed during the night to care for his old teacher.

By courtesy of RCPI

By courtesy of RCPI

18.1   Edward Halloran Bennett (1837-1907)
*Bennett was known in Sir Patrick Dun's Hospital as
'The Boss'. 'He walked the wards with one shoulder
raised, a somewhat whimsical expression on his
countenance, and from time to time dropped gems of
clinical knowledge, especially in connection with fractures
and diseases of the bone.' (Moorehead)*

18.2   William Stokes in old age
*'Amid all the ardour of clinical observation and research
he never for one moment forgot the sufferer before him —
no thoughtless word from his lips, no rough or unkind
action every ruffled the calm confidence reposed in him by
those who sought his skill and care.'*

J W Moore (1878) in *Dublin Journal of Medical Science*

152

CHAPTER 18

End of an Era

The relationship between the success of the Dublin school and its dynamic founder members is emphasised by the fact that Robert Smith continued to serve as secretary of the Pathological Society of Dublin from its establishment in 1838 until his death in 1873. During that time he was also a regular contributor to the meetings. Smith was succeeded as professor of surgery in the School of Physic by Edward Halloran Bennett, who also succeeded Smith as secretary of the Pathological Society of Dublin and as surgeon to Sir Patrick Dun's Hospital.

Bennett was born in Cork in 1837 and studied medicine in the School of Physic in Dublin. He graduated in 1859 and became a fellow of the Royal College of Surgeons in 1863. He served initially as an assistant surgeon in Sir Patrick Dun's Hospital where he was influenced greatly by Robert Smith. In later life he never tired of telling anecdotes about Smith to his students. He inherited Smith's enthusiasm for orthopaedics and in 1881 at a meeting of the Pathological Society of Dublin he described for the first time the well known fracture of the base of the first metacarpal bone, which is now known as Bennett's Fracture.

During Bennett's period as secretary of the Dublin Pathological Society, definite plans were made to amalgamate it with three other medical societies in the city to form an Academy of Medicine. The other societies involved were the Dublin Society of Surgeons, the Medical Society of the College of Physicians and the Dublin Obstetrical Society. In 1878 a postal vote revealed that the vast majority of the members of the four societies were in favour of amalgamation. Each of the societies was to become a section within the new academy. In 1882 the new Academy of Medicine met for the first time and the Pathological Society of Dublin became the Section of Pathology. Pasteur and Von Recklinghausen were among the first honorary fellows elected by the new academy. In 1982 the Royal Academy of Medicine in Ireland celebrated its centenary and marked the occasion with a special centenary issue of the *Irish Journal of Medical Science.*

The last meeting of the Pathological Society of Dublin took place on 25 March 1882. The minutes of the society show that the last case was presented by a young doctor named Bertram Windle. He was a grandnephew of Sir Philip Crampton and became a gifted polymath who played a key role in the creation of the University of Birmingham. Windle became president of University College Cork later in his career and he had a major impact on the development of its medical school.

Although Irish medicine produced a number of outstanding men during the later years of the last century, its international standing began to decline. William Stokes was aware that the school was losing its impetus during his last years. The explanation most commonly given to account for this decline was that the members of the school failed to keep abreast of developments in the more technical aspects of medicine, a view that was certainly held by Stokes. Addressing a meeting of the Medical Society of the College of Physicians in Dublin on 16 November 1870 he said:

> It is admitted on all hands that during the last half century a great school of Practical Medicine, Surgery and Midwifery, has in Dublin grown to such dimensions, and established such a character, as to constitute at least one source of legitimate national pride, so much wanting in Ireland; a possession which to any country is more to be valued than wealth or power, or the barbarous triumphs of war.
>
> But to all thinking men who have watched the rise, progress, and actual state of the Irish School of Medicine, the question presents itself — Are we, so far as modern methods of research are concerned, keeping up with the progress of medical science? Are we standing still and drawing on our acquired prestige? or if advancing, are we not following merely the beaten path, irrespective of the growth of knowledge in other places?[1]

Stokes went on to analyse the state of medicine in Dublin and he concluded that it lagged behind in its scientific rather than its clinical aspects. Referring to the Pathological Society of Dublin he pointed out that it had been growing and expanding for more than thirty years yet microscopy and pathological chemistry comprised a comparatively small part of the proceedings:

> Have we afforded our students the primary instruction or even the means of teaching themselves, or showing them that knowledge, which implies power, is advancing all around us and them, while we or they are standing

still or advancing but in one groove? Or have they been shown the excellence of labouring for truth for its own sake, irrespective of its immediate consequences?

We may put aside the ophthalmoscope, the laryngoscope, the stethoscope, and the endoscope, which last, thanks to the labours of Dr Cruise, Dublin may almost claim for her own, and pass to the microscope, the spectroscope and chemical research.[1]

He then detailed the great advances made on the Continent in laboratory medicine and in the use of the microscope. He praised the hospital laboratories of Vienna, Berlin, Breslau and Stockholm and he advocated that similar laboratories should be attached to all the Dublin hospitals. Stokes went on to propose a training in basic science for all students, and the appointment of doctors to oversee the developments of the hospital laboratories and to act as 'referee or consultant to physician or surgeon in every case requiring advanced physical investigation'.[1] Such appointments he said were being made in most of the London hospitals and the first one in Dublin had just been made at the Mater Hospital. In 1873 Dr Steevens' Hospital appointed Chichester Bell, cousin of Alexander Graham Bell, the inventor of the telephone, as a 'Pathological Analyst'. He was professor of botany and later of chemistry in the medical school which was attached to the hospital at that time. As his specific duty in the hospital was the analysis of morbid products, he was one of the first chemical pathologists in Ireland. Bell resigned in 1877 and went first to University College London and later to Boston where he worked with his cousin in the laboratory of the Bell Telephone Company.

The last book that Stokes wrote was a biography of his life long friend, the artist George Petrie. This work was a labour of love for Stokes. It was published in 1868 and was a major undertaking of over four hundred pages. On receiving his copy the Earl of Dunraven wrote to Stokes from his home in Adare, County Limerick:

Thanks for the delightful book which came this morning. I am very glad you did not write my name, as you will have to come and do it here, and the sooner the better.

Do not trouble yourself about the omissions of your book. If the public is worthy of the work they can be inserted in due time. And in the meantime be content with having paid the noblest tribute that could be offered to your departed friend, and paid it so handsomely and satisfactorily I really quite envy you — if such a feeling is allowable; as a friend I am truly proud of the result of your labours, and as Petrie's friend I warmly thank you for having with such truth, such feeling, and such thorough appreciation done honour to one of Ireland's most gifted heroes.[2]

On 17 March 1874 Stokes was nominated to the presidency of the Royal Irish Academy. In the same year he received the degree LL D *honoris causa* from the University of Cambridge. Two years later he was honoured like Corrigan when he saw his statue by the sculptor J H Foley being unveiled in the College of Physicians. In the same year he received another great honour, a German knighthood, when the ambassador of the German emperor, William I, presented him with the Prussian Order 'Pour le Mérite' of Frederick the Great. This was an honour which had never previously been conferred on a medical author. Originally awarded only for military services on the field of battle, after 1842 it was also awarded for outstanding proficiency in science and art.

Although now over seventy years of age Stokes continued to practise medicine and to do house calls. However, while travelling to see a patient in County Wicklow he fell from his carriage. He became very incapacitated after this and was forced to retire to his country home, Carraig Breac, at Howth. Here he spent the time remaining to him with his daughter Margaret. He received frequent visits from his friends, many of them former pupils, and he spent much of his time reading.

> Music, ballad, poetry, his plantations and flower garden, and observing the beautiful and ever changing effects of mist and cloud, sunshine and shadow on the bay beneath him, and the fair Wicklow hills beyond, were all sources of deep delight.[3]

His health deteriorated suddenly in November 1877 when he had a stroke and he died two months later on 6 January 1878. It was his wish to be buried in the ancient churchyard of Saint Fintan on the western slope of the Hill of Howth. On a bright frosty morning the local countrypeople carried the remains from Carraig Breac to the churchyard. A large crowd attended and the procession, led by fifty students from the Meath Hospital, made its way slowly to the ruins of the ivy-clad church. When they reached the church the coffin was placed on the shoulders of eight students and was borne by them to the graveside. It was a fitting tribute to the man who had, with his colleagues of the Irish school, made Dublin one of the great medical centres of Europe.

The deaths of Stokes and Corrigan marked the end of a remarkable era in medicine. However, the nineteenth-century Irish school of medicine has left a heritage which is still cherished in the country's hospitals and medical schools. It also contributed to the foundation of modern clinical teaching in Europe and North America. The strength of the Irish school lay in the high standards of its clinical teachers. These men placed the patient at the centre of their teaching and they exhorted their students to strive for excellence. They emphasised the importance of original research and the number of clinical conditions which bear their names testifies to their success in this area. Robert Graves expressed the spirit of the school when concluding the final lecture of his course in clinical medicine. This lecture forms the last chapter of his textbook *Clinical Lectures on the Practice of Medicine* which was first published in 1843 when the school was at the height of its fame:

> I have done now, the session is over, and I must conclude. It was usual in my time to spend five or ten minutes at the termination of a closing lecture in flattering the class and indulging in a complimentary strain. I do not mean to do this. I cannot say that you have been idle; but, gentlemen, we cannot be too industrious. Never was there a time when the career of science was so brilliant and so rapid as the present: there never was a time when the inducements were so great to explore, investigate, and treasure up the numerous and deeply interesting mass of facts for which science is indebted to modern discovery. The day is gone by when quackery could impose upon the credulous, and impudence assume the garb of merit; a century ago it was very easy to keep up with the scanty and slow-paced intelligence of the age; men became acquainted with certain opinions which they regarded as fixed and immutable, and here their pursuit of science was abandoned. In our times the field of science is so broad and extensive, and its increase on every side so rapid and so various that he who wishes not to be left completely behind must employ all his energies with continuous and unremitting assiduity.[4]

Notes

CHAPTER 1

1. B O'Meara. 1852. *Napoleon in Exile or A Voice from St Helena*, New York, p 5

CHAPTER 2

1. A Macalister. 1900. *James Macartney*. Hodder and Stoughton, London, p 114
2. *Ibid.* p 93
3. *Ibid.* p 111
4. *Ibid.* p 139
5. J Cheyne. 1818. 'A case of apoplexy in which the fleshy part of the heart was converted into fat', in *Dublin Hospital Reports*, 2, 216-23

CHAPTER 3

1. W Stokes (ed.). 1863. 'The life and labours of Graves', in *Studies in Physiology and Medicine* by the late Robert Graves. Churchill, London, p xii
2. H W Acland. 1882. 'Memoir of William Stokes', in *Diseases of the Chest* by William Stokes, ed. A Hudson. The New Syndenham Society, London, p xx
3. R J Graves. 1864. *Clinical Lectures on the Practice of Medicine*, ed. J M Nelligan. Fannin, Dublin, p 8
4. L H Ormsby. 1892. *Medical History of the Meath Hospital and County Infirmary*. Fannin, Dublin, p 36
5. *Ibid.* p 37
6. *Ibid.* p 40
7. W Stokes (ed.). 1863. 'The life and labours of Graves', in *Studies in Physiology and Medicine* by the late Robert Graves. Churchill, London, p xx
8. R J Graves. 1824. 'Report of the fever lately prevalent in Galway', in *Transactions of the Association of Fellows and Licentiates*, IV, 408-438
9. W R Wilde. 1842. 'Robert James Graves', in *Dublin University Magazine*, XXVII, 260-273
10. Erinensis (P H Green). 1828. 'Opening of the medical session in Dublin', in *The Lancet*, 8 Nov 1828. Reproduced in *The Sketches of Erinensis*, ed. M Fallon, pp 198-209. Skilton and Shaw, London, pp 198-209
11. R J Graves. 1864. *Clinical Lectures on the Practice of Medicine*, ed. J M Nelligan. Fannin, Dublin, p 9
12. J W Moore. 1878. 'In memoriam. William Stokes', in *Dublin Journal of Medical Science*, 65, 186-200
13. R J Graves. 1864. *Clinical Lectures on the Practice of Medicine*, ed. J M Nelligan. Fannin, Dublin, p 7
14. W Stokes (ed.). 1863. 'The life and labours of Graves', in *Studies in Physiology and Medicine* by the late Robert Graves. Churchill, London, p xli
15. E O'Brien. 1984. 'The Royal College of Surgeons in Ireland: A bicentennial tribute', in *Irish Journal of Medical Science*, 13, 1, 29-34
16. R J Graves. 1835. 'Newly observed affection of the thyroid gland in females', in *London Medical and Surgical Journal*, VII, pt 2, 516-517
17. L H Ormsby. 1892. *Medical History of the Meath Hospital and County Infirmary*. Fannin, Dublin, p 128

CHAPTER 4

1. W T Tone. 1826. *Life of Theobald Wolfe Tone*, ed. by his son. Gales and Seaton, Washington, p 31

2. H W Acland. 1882. 'Memoir of William Stokes', in *Diseases of the Chest* by William Stokes, ed. A Hudson. The New Syndenham Society, London, p x

3. *Ibid.* p x

4. L H Ormsby. 1892. *Medical History of the Meath Hospital and County Infirmary*. Fannin, Dublin, p 38

5. W Stokes (ed). 1863. 'The life and labours of Graves', in *Studies in Physiology and Medicine* by the late Robert Graves. Churchill, London, p xviii

6. W Stokes. 1898. *William Stokes. His Life and Works*. Fisher Unwin, London, pp 43-44

7. W Stokes. 1828. *Two Lectures on the Application of the Stethoscope to the Diagnosis and Treatment of Thoracic Disease*. Hodges and McArthur, Dublin, p 55

8. W Doolin. 1947. *Wayfarers In Medicine*. Heinemann, London, p 261

9. W Stokes. 1898. *William Stokes. His Life and Works*. Fisher Unwin, London, pp 45-46

10. J D H Widdess. 1972. *The Richmond, Whitworth and Hardwicke Hospitals 1772-1972*. Dublin, p 62

11. W Stokes. 1898. *William Stokes. His Life and Works*. Fisher Unwin, London, p 100

12. *Ibid.* p 101

13. *Ibid.* p 104

CHAPTER 5

1. M Fallon. 1972. *Abraham Colles (1773-1843)*. William Heinemann Medical Books, London, p 45

2. A Colles. 1814. 'On the fracture of the carpal extremity of the radius', in *Edinburgh Medical and Surgical Journal*, 10, 182

3. R W Smith. 1847. *Treatise on Fractures in the Vicinity of Joints*. Hodges and Smith, Dublin, p 129

4. M Fallon. 1972. *Abraham Colles (1773-1843)*. William Heinemann Medical Books, London, p 167

5. Review of *Practical Observations on the Venereal Disease and on the Use of Mercury* by A Colles, in *The Lancet*, II, 23-24

6. W Wallace. 1837. 'Clinical lectures and remarks on diseases of the skin, venereal diseases and surgical cases', in *The Lancet*, II, 534-540

7. 'Death notice of William Wallace' in *The Lancet*, I, 524

8. W Stokes. 1846. 'Observations on the case of the late Abraham Colles', in *Dublin Quarterly Journal of Medical Science*, 1, 303

9. R W Smith. 1846. 'Account of the post-mortem examination of the body of the late Abraham Colles Esq. MD. Communicated to the Pathological Society of Dublin', 9 December 1843, in *Dublin Quarterly Journal of Medical Science*, 1, 311

10. A Jacob. 1819. 'An account of a membrane in the eye, now first described' in *Philosophical Translations*, 109, 300-307

11. A Jacob. 1827. 'Observations respecting an ulcer of peculiar character which attacks the eyelid and other parts of the face', in *Dublin Hospital Reports*, 4, 232-39

12. A Jacob. 1850. *On the Operation for the Removal of Cataract as Performed with a Fine Sewing Needle through the Cornea*. Medical Press Office, Dublin, pp 21-22

13. C A Cameron. 1886. *History of the Royal College of Surgeons in Ireland*. Fannin, Dublin, p 391

14. R J Graves. 1864. *Clinical Lectures on the Practice of Medicine*, ed. J M Nelligan. Fannin, Dublin, p 5

CHAPTER 6

1. 'Transactions of the medical society of the College of Physicians', in *Dublin Journal of Medical Science*, LXV, 239
2. 'William Stokes MD. FRS.'(Obituary, 1878), in *British Medical Journal*, I, 63
3. W Stokes (ed). 1863. 'The life and labours of Graves', in *Studies in Physiology and Medicine by the late Robert Graves*. Churchill, London, p xxxiv
4. W Stokes. 1840. *Clinical Lectures on the Theory and Practice of Medicine*, ed. John Bell. Barrington and Haswell, Philadelphia
5. D J Corrigan. 1837. Review of William Stokes' treatise on diseases of the chest, in *Dublin Journal of Medical Science*, XI, 466
6. J C Ferguson. 1824-25. *Diary Manuscript*. D 1918/2/4. Public Records Office Northern Ireland, Belfast, p 1
7. *Ibid.* p 8
8. *Ibid.* p 30
9. *Ibid.* p 28
10. J C Ferguson. 1830. 'Auscultation, the only unequivocal evidence of pregnancy', in *Dublin Medical Transactions*, 1, 64

CHAPTER 7

1. D J Corrigan. 1879. 'Reminiscences of a medical student prior to the passing of the Anatomy Act', in *British Medical Journal*, 1, 59-60
2. J Macartney. 1828. 'Example of leaving the body for dissection', in *London Medical Gazette*, 1, 637
3. J D H Widdess. 1963. *A History of the Royal College of Physicians of Ireland*. Livingstone, Edinburgh and London, p 185
4. D Corrigan. 1838. *Address Delivered at the Opening Meeting of the Dublin Medico-Chirurgical Society Session of 1837-38*. Hodges and Smith, Dublin, p 16
5. R Adams. 1827. 'Cases of diseases of the heart accompanied with pathological observations', in *Dublin Hospitals Reports*, IV, 353
6. R Adams. 1860. 'Richmond, Whitworth and Hardwicke hospitals', in *Dublin Hospital Gazette*, 7, 321-324

CHAPTER 8

1. C A Cameron. 1886. *History of the Royal College of Surgeons in Ireland*. Fannin, Dublin, p 661
2. 'Scientific intelligence' (1839) in *Dublin Journal of Medical Science*, XIV, 548
3. First Report of the Council (1839), Dublin Pathological Society, Dublin
4. 'Proceedings of the Pathological Society of Dublin', in *Dublin Journal of Medical Science*, XV, 144-160
5. *Ibid.* XV, 498-501
6. F Cruise. 1912. *Sir Dominic Corrigan*. Catholic Truth Society, London, p 9
7. W Stokes. 1898. *William Stokes. His Life and Works*. Fisher Unwin, London, p 126

CHAPTER 9

1. W R Wilde. 1839. *Narrative of a Voyage to Madeira, Teneriffe and Along the Shores of the Mediterranean*. Curry, Dublin, p 267
2. *Ibid.* p 271
3. A Macalister, 1900. *James Macartney*. Hodder and Stoughton, London, p 247

4. *Ibid.* p 274
5. W R Wilde. 1843. *Austria. Its Literary, Scientific and Medical Institutions.* Curry, Dublin, p 183
6. W R Wilde. 1853. *Practical Observations on Aural Surgery and the Nature and Treatment of Diseases of the Ear*, Churchill, London
7. W R Wilde. 1846. 'The editor's preface', in *Dublin Quarterly Journal of Medical Science*, I,I, i-xlviii
8. A Macalister. 1900. *James Macartney.* Hodder and Stoughton, London, p 163

CHAPTER 10
1. W Stokes. 1898. *William Stokes. His Life and Works.* Fisher Unwin, London, p 113
2. R J Graves. 1863. *Studies in Physiology and Medicine*, ed. W Stokes. Churchill, London, p lvi
3. *Ibid.* p 132
4. R J Graves. 1864. *Clinical Lectures on the Practice of Medicine*, ed. J M Nelligan. Fannin, Dublin, p 74
5. T A Emmet. 1911. *Incidents of My Life.* Putmans, New York and London, p 139
6. R J Rowlette. 1939. *The Medical Press and Circular.* London, p 38
7. R J Graves. 1847. 'A Letter to the editor, relative to the proceedings of the Central Board of Health of Ireland', in *Dublin Quarterly Journal of Medical Science*, 4, 513-544
8. R J Graves. 1849. 'On the progress of Asiatic cholera', in *Dublin Quarterly Journal of Medical Science*, VII, 1-39
9. R J Graves. 1850. 'Observations on cholera and especially on its mode of propagation', in *Dublin Quarterly Journal of Medical Science*, X, 20, 257-286
10. W Stokes (ed). 1863. 'The life and labours of Graves', in *Studies in Physiology and Medicine* by the late Robert Graves. Churchill, London, p xvi
11. R J Graves. 1837. 'Letter to Corrigan', in the Corrigan Papers, Royal College of Surgeons in Ireland
12. 'Sir Dominic John Corrigan' (Obituary, 1880), in *Dublin Journal of Medical Science*, 69, 268-272
13. W Stokes. 1898. *William Stokes. His Life and Works.* Fisher Unwin, London, p 115

CHAPTER 11
1. J MacDonnell. 1847. 'Amputation of the arm performed at the Richmond Hospital without pain', in *Dublin Medical Press*, 18, 8-9
2. A pupil of the College of Surgeons in Ireland. 1825. 'The Dublin hospitals' (letter), in *The Lancet*, VIII, 6, 179-180
3. J Houston. 1844. 'The microscopic pathology of cancer', in *Dublin Medical Press*, 12, 5-8
4. J Houston. 1830. 'Observations on the mucous membrane of the rectum', in *Dublin Hospital Reports*, 5, 158-165
5. F Rynd. 1849. *Pathological and Practical Observations on Stricture and some Other Diseases of the Male Urethra.* Longmans, London
6. F Rynd. 1845. 'Neuralgia — Introduction of fluid to the nerve', in *Dublin Medical Press*, 12 March, CCCXXIII, 167-168
7. L H Ormsby. 1892. *Medical History of the Meath Hospital and County Infirmary.* Fannin, Dublin, p 209
8. J D H Widdess. 1951. 'Dublin hospitals — A century's progress', in *Adelaide Hospital Centenary Book*, p 41
9. W Wilde. 1846. 'The editor's preface', in *Dublin Quarterly Journal of Medical Science*, 1,1, xlvi
10. C A Cameron. 1886. *History of the Royal College of Surgeons in Ireland.* Fannin, Dublin, p 632

11. F Cruise. 1912. *Sir Dominic Corrigan*. Catholic Truth Society, p 8
12. W Stokes. 1866. 'An address delivered before the medical society of the King and Queen's College of Physicians in Ireland', in *The Medical Press and Circular*, ii, 609-611
13. C A Cameron. 1886. *History of the Royal College of Surgeons in Ireland*. Fannin, Dublin, p 571

CHAPTER 12
1. W J Sinclair. 1909. *Semmelweis: His Life and Doctrine*. Manchester, p 48
2. W F Montgomery. 1837. *An Exposition of the Signs and Symptoms of Pregnancy*. Sherwood, Gilbert and Piper, London, p 61
3. L Atthill. 1911. *Recollections of An Irish Doctor*. Religious Tract Society, London, p 203
4. E Kennedy. 1839. 'Introductory address delivered at the first meeting of the Dublin Obstetrical Society', in *Dublin Journal of Medical Science*, XV, 160-178
5. Report of the Select Committee on Dublin Hospitals (1854), p 196
6. *Ibid.* p 195
7. E B Sinclair and G Johnston. 1858. *Practical Midwifery*. London, p 8
8. *Ibid.* p 10
9. *Ibid.* p 11

CHAPTER 13
1. D Corrigan. 1857. 'Valedictory presidential address to the Pathological Society', in *Dublin Hospital Gazette*, 4, 139-141
2. Report of the Select Committee on Dublin Hospitals (1854), p 197
3. D Reisman. 1922. 'The Dublin medical school and its influence upon medicine in America', in *Annals of Medical History*, 4, 86-96
4. H Cushing. 1940. *The Life of Sir William Osler*. Oxford University Press, London, p 1008
5. *Ibid.* p 63
6. *Ibid.* p 83
7. *Ibid.* p 698
8. O W Holmes. 1883. *Medical Essays*. Houghton Mufflin, Boston, p 298
9. E Bendiner. 1984. 'The Dublin school: from poverty, a rich legacy, in *Hospital Practice*, June, 221-247
10. D Reisman. 1922. 'The Dublin medical school and its influence upon medicine in America', in *Annals of Medical History*, 4, 86-96

CHAPTER 14
1. R B McDowell. 1985. 'The main narrative' in *The Royal Irish Academy (1785-1985)*, ed. T O'Raifeartaigh. The Royal Irish Academy, Dublin, p 22
2. R J Graves. 1863. *Studies in Physiology and Medicine*, ed. W Stokes. Churchill, London, p xix
3. W Stokes. 1898. *William Stokes. His Life and Works*. Fisher Unwin, London, p 79
4. J P Mahaffy. 1878. 'Dr William Stokes: A personal sketch', in *Macmillan's Magazine*, 37, 299-303
5. W Stokes. 1868. *The Life and Labours in Art and Archaeology of George Petrie*. Longmans, London, p 317
6. W Stokes. 1898. *William Stokes. His Life and Works*. Fisher Unwin, London, p 190
7. T Carlyle. 1882. *Reminiscences of my Irish Journey in 1849*. Sampson Low, London, p 41
8. L Atthill. 1911. *Recollections of an Irish Doctor*. Religious Tract Society, London, p 195
9. W Stokes. 1898. *William Stokes. His Life and Works*. Fisher Unwin, London, p 90

10. J P Mahaffy. 1878. 'Dr William Stokes: A personal sketch', in *Macmillan's Magazine*, 37, 299-303

11. W Stokes. 1898. *William Stokes. His Life and Works*. Fisher Unwin, London, p 248

12. W J O'Driscoll. 1871. *A Memoir of Daniel Maclise*. Longmans, Green, London, p 17

13. C A Cameron. 1913. *Reminiscences of Sir Charles A Cameron*. Dublin and London, p 48

14. Lotten von Kraemer. 1902. 'Författaren Oscar Wilde's Föräldrahem i Irlands Hufvudstad.' *Ordch Bild*, 429-35. Quoted in *Oscar Wilde* by Richard Elmann, London, p 17

15. R J Rowlette. 1939. *The Medical Press and Circular*. London, p 63

16. *Ibid.*

17. Minutes of the Medico-Philosophical Society, Royal College of Physicians of Ireland

CHAPTER 15

1. L H Ormsby. 1892. *Medical History of the Meath Hospital and County Infirmary*. Fannin, Dublin, p 124

2. R J Graves. 1864. *Clinical Lectures on the Practice of Medicine*, ed. J M Nelligan. Fannin, Dublin, p 9

3. C A Cameron. 1886. *History of the Royal College of Surgeons in Ireland*. Fannin, Dublin, p 590

4. Nora Robertson. 1960. *Crowned Harp*. Allen Figgis, Dublin, p 30

5. *Ibid.* p 27

6. W R Wilde. 1853. *Practical Observations on Aural Surgery and the Nature and Treatment of Diseases of the Ear*, Churchill, London, p 424

7. J F Duncan. 1878. 'The life and labours of Robert Graves', in *The Dublin Journal of Medical Science*, LXV, 1-12

CHAPTER 16

1. W Stokes. 1854. *Diseases of the Heart and the Aorta*. Hodges and Smith, Dublin

2. *Ibid.* p 132

3. *Ibid.* p 336

4. *Ibid.* p 357

5. W Hale-White. 1935. *Great Doctors of the Nineteenth Century*. Edward Arnold, London, p 137

6. W Stokes. 1872. 'A discourse on state medicine', in *British Medical Journal*, 13 April, 385-389

7. W Stokes. 1898. *William Stokes. His Life and Works*. Fisher Unwin, London, p 173

CHAPTER 17

1. F Cruise. 1912. *Sir Dominic Corrigan*. Catholic Truth Society, p 8

2. D Corrigan, *Diaries*. Royal College of Physicians of Ireland, no 6, p 33

3. *Ibid.* no 6, p 35

4. *Ibid.* no 4, p 8

CHAPTER 18

1. W Stokes. 1871. 'On some requirements in clinical teaching in Dublin', in *Dublin Quarterly Journal of Medical Science*, 51, 38-52

2. W Stokes. 1898. *William Stokes. His Life and Works*. Fisher Unwin, London, p 227

3. *Ibid.* p 237

4. R J Graves. 1864. *Clinical Lectures on the Practice of Medicine*, ed. J M Nelligan. Fannin, Dublin, p 860

Select Bibliography

ADAMS, R. 1939. 'Biography and bibliography', in *Medical Classic*, III, 6, 620-697. William and Wilkins, Baltimore

CHEYNE, J. 1843. *Essay on Partial Derangement of the Mind in Supposed Connexion With Religion.* Curry, Dublin
 1886. *Pettigrews Medical Portraits.* London
 1839. 'Biography and bibliography', in *Medical Classics*, III, 7, 698-704. William and Wilkins, Baltimore

COAKLEY, D and M. 1985. *Wit and Wine, Literary and Artistic Cork in the Nineteenth Century.* Glendale Press, Dublin

COLLES, A. 1939. 'Biography and bibliography of Colles', in *Medical Classics*, IV, 1026-1078. William and Wilkins, Baltimore

COLLINS, R. 1835. *A Practical Treatise on Midwifery, Containing the Result of Sixteen Thousand Six Hundred and Fifty-Four Births Occurring in the Dublin Lying-In Hospital During a Period of Seven Years Commencing November, 1826.* London

CORRIGAN D J. 1832. 'On permanent patency of the mouth of the aorta, or inadequacy of the aortic valves', in *Edinburgh Medical and Surgical Journal*, 37, 225-245
 1936. 'Biography and bibliography of Corrigan', in *Medical Classics*, 1, 673-730. William and Wilkins, Baltimore

CUMMINS, N M A. 1959. 'Medicine in southern Éire. A Cork medical pioneer', in *Journal of the Irish Medical Association*, 165-170

CRUISE, F R. 1865. 'The utility of the endoscope as an aid in the diagnosis and treatment of disease', in *Dublin Quarterly Journal of Medical Science*, 39, 329
 1887. *Thomas a Kempis*, Kegan Paul, Trench, London
 1912. *Catholic Men of Science*, ed. Bertram Windle. Catholic Truth Society, London

De VERE WHITE, T. 1967. *The Parents of Oscar Wilde.* Hodder and Stoughton, London

DOOLIN, W. 1987. *Dublin's Surgeon — Anatomists and Other Essays*, ed. J B Lyons. Dublin

DOOLIN, W and FITZGERALD, O (Eds). 1952. *What's Past is Prologue.* Dublin.

DUNRAVEN, EARL OF, (W QUINN). 1875. *Notes on Irish Architecture*, ed. M Stokes. Bell and Sons, London

FALLON, M. 1972. *Abraham Colles (1773-1843).* William Heinemann Medical Books, London
 1979. *The Sketches of Erinensis.* Skilton and Shaw, Dublin
'First Report of the Council (1839).' Dublin Pathological Society, Dublin

FLEETWOOD, J F. 1983. *The History of Medicine in Ireland.* Skellig Press, Dublin

FLEMING, J B. 1966. 'The teaching of midwifery in the University of Dublin', in *Hermathena* 1966, CIII 66-81

FROGGATT, P. 1965. 'Sir William Wilde and the 1851 census of Ireland', in *Medical History*, IX, 4, 302-327
 1965. 'The demographic work of Sir William Wilde', in *Irish Journal of Medical Science*, IX, May, 213-230

GRAVES, R J. 1941. 'Biography and bibliography of Graves', in *Medical Classics*, V, 22-45. William and Wilkins, Baltimore

GRAVES, R J and STOKES, W. 1827. *Clinical Reports of the Medical Cases in The Meath Hospital 1826, 1827.* Graisberry, Dublin

JESSOP, W J E. 1973. 'Samuel Haughton: a Victorian polymath', in *Hermathena*, 2-26

KIRKPATRICK, T P C. 1912. *History of the Medical Teaching in Trinity College Dublin*. Hanna and Neale, Dublin
    1913. 'Diary of an Irish medical student 1831-37', in *Dublin Journal of Medical Science*, 360-378
    1924. *The History of Doctor Steevens' Hospital Dublin*. Dublin
    1926. 'Centenary address on the history of the School of Physic Trinity College Dublin', in *Irish Journal of Medical Science*, 3, 114-120
    1937. 'The Royal Academy of Medicine in Ireland', in *The Medical Press and Circular*, CXCV 180-184
KIRKPATRICK, T P C and JELLET, H. 1913. *The Book of the Rotunda Hospital*. Adalard, London

LOGAN, P. 1984. *Medical Dublin*. Apple-tree Press, Belfast
LYONS, J B. 1976. 'Sir William Wilde', in *Journal of the Irish College of Physics and Surgery*, 5, 4, 147-152
    1978. *Brief Lives of Irish Doctors*, Blackwater, Dublin
LYONS, A S and PETRUCELLI, R J. 1978. *Medicine. An Illustrated History*. Abrahams, New York

MacARTHUR, W P. 1956. *Medical History of the Famine in the Great Famine*, eds. R Dudley Edwards and T D Williams. Browne and Nolan, Dublin
MacDONNELL, H H G. 1889. *Some Notes on the Graves Family (For Private Circulation)*. Dublin
MAHAFFY, J P. 1892. *The Book of Trinity College*. Hodges and Figgis, Dublin
MAJOR, R H. 1945. *Classic Descriptions of Disease*. Charles Thomas, Illinois
MEENAN, F O C. 1968. 'The Victorian doctors of Dublin', in *Irish Journal of Medical Science*, 1,7,311-320
    1978. 'The medical consultants of Dublin — A social and political portrait', in *Essays in Honour of J D H Widdess*, ed. Eoin O'Brien, 57-67. Dublin
    1987. *Cecilia Street*. Gill and Macmillan Ltd, Dublin
'Minutes of the Medico-Philosophical Society.' Royal College of Physicians of Ireland
MOORE, J W. 1897. 'Irish medical schools', in *British Medical Journal*, 1, 1629
    1912. 'Francis Cruise' (Obituary), in *Irish Journal of Medical Science*, 133, 314
MOOREHEAD, T G. 1935. *British Masters of Medicine*. William Stokes, Medical Press, 191: 130-133
    1942. *A Short History of Sir Patrick Dun's Hospital*. Dublin
MORTON, L T. 1983. *A Medical Bibliography*. London

O'BRIEN, E. 1983. *Conscience and Conflict, A Biography of Sir Dominic Corrigan*. Glendale Press, Dublin
O'BRIEN, E (ed). 1978. *Essays in Honour of J D H Widdess*. Dublin
    1987. *The Charitable Infirmary Jervis Street — A Farewell Tribute 1718-1987*. The Anniversary Press, Dublin
O'BRIEN, E, CROOKSHANK, A, WOLSTENHOLME, G. 1984. *A Portrait of Irish Medicine*. Dublin
O'RAIFEARTAIGH, T. 1985. *The Royal Irish Academy*, Dublin
O'RAGHALLAIGH, D. 1942. *Sir Robert Kane*, Cork University Press
O'RAHILLY, R. 1948. 'Edward Hallaran Bennett (1837-1907)', in *Irish Journal of Medical Science*, 267, 127-131
    1948. *Benjamin Alcock*. Cork University Press, Cork

PINKERTON, J H M. 1981. 'John Creery Ferguson', in *Ulster Medical Journal*, 50, 10-20
PUSEY, W A. 1933. *The History and Epidemiology of Syphilis*. Charles Thomas, Illinois

REISMAN, D. 1913. 'The great Irish clinicians of the nineteenth century', in *Johns Hopkins Hospital Bulletin*, 270, 251-257

ROSS, I C. 1986. *Public Virtue, Public Love*. The O'Brien Press, Dublin

RYND, F. 1845. 'Neuralgia — Introduction of fluid to the nerve', in *Dublin Medical Press*, 12 March, CCCXXIII, 167-168

   1849. *Pathological and Practical Observations on Stricture and some Other Diseases of the Male Urethra*. Longmans, London

   1861. 'Description of an instrument for the subcutaneous introduction of fluids in affections of the nerves', in *Dublin Quarterly Journal of Medical Science*, 32, 13

SCHMID, L. 1968. 'Irish doctors in Bohemia', in *Irish Journal of Medical Science*, 1, 11, 497-504

SMITH, R W. 1847. *Treatise on Fractures in the Vicinity of the Joints*. Dublin

SNELLEN, H A. 1984. *History of Cardiology*. Donker Academic Publications, Rotterdam

STOKES, WILLIAM. 1837. *On the Diagnosis and Treatment of Diseases of the Chest*. Hodges and Smith, Dublin

   1846. 'Observations on some cases of permanently slow pulse', in *Dublin Quarterly Journal of Medical Science*, 11, 111, 73-85

   1854. 'A discourse on the life and works of the late Robert James Graves', in *Medical Times and Gazette*, 184, 1-5

   1882. *Diseases of the Chest with Memoir by Dr Acland*, ed. A Hudson. New Syndenham Society, London

   1939. 'Biography and bibliography', in *Medical Classics*, III, 710-738. William and Wilkins, Baltimore

STOKES, WHITLEY. 1845. 'Biography', in *Dublin University Magazine*, XXVI 202-10

STORY, J B. 1918. 'Sir William Robert Wills Wilde. British masters of ophthalmology', in *British Journal of Ophthalmology*, 2, 65-71

TAYLOR, M. 1932. *Bertram Windle*. Longmans, London

WALLACE, W. 1833. *A Treatise on the Venereal Disease and its Varieties*. London

   1835. 'Contagion of secondary syphilis', in *The Lancet*, I, 805

   1836. 'Treatment of the venereal disease by the hydriodate of potash, or iodide of potassium', in *The Lancet*, 2, 5-11

   1836. 'Lectures on cutaneous and venereal diseases', in *The Lancet*, 11, 129-133

   1837. 'The structure of the Negro's skin', in *The Lancet*, 1, 299-304, 339-344, 370-376

WIDDESS, J D H. 1948. 'The beginning of medical microscopy in Ireland', in *Irish Journal of Medical Science*, 274, 668-678

   1949. *The Schools of Surgery*. Livingstone, Edinburgh

   1968. 'Cruise's endoscope', in *Journal of the Royal College of Surgeons in Ireland*, 4, 156-157

   1968. 'An historic surgical instrument', in *Journal of the Royal College of Surgeons in Ireland*, 4, 13

   1984. *The Royal College of Surgeons in Ireland and its Medical School*. Dublin

WILDE, W R. 1864. *Memoir of Robert J Graves*. McGlashan and Gill, Dublin

   1849. *The Beauties of the Boyne, and its Tributary the Blackwater*. McGlashan, Dublin

   1867. *Lough Corrib, its Shores and Islands: With Notices of Lough Mask*. McGlashan and Gill, Dublin

WILSON, T G. 1942. *Victorian Doctor*. Methuen, London

Index